This book is part of the Allyn and Bacon Series in Creative Teaching.
The books in this series are:

I

Setting Conditions for Creative Teaching in the Elementary School
James A. Smith

II

Creative Teaching of the Language Arts
in the Elementary School
James A. Smith

III

Creative Teaching of Reading and Literature
in the Elementary School
James A. Smith

IV

Creative Teaching of the Creative Arts
in the Elementary School
James A. Smith

V

Creative Teaching of the Social Studies
in the Elementary School
James A. Smith

VI

Creative Teaching of Mathematics
in the Elementary School
Alvin M. Westcott and James A. Smith

VII

Creative Teaching of Science
in the Elementary School
Albert Piltz and Robert Sund

Creativity begins with wonder.

Creative Teaching of Mathematics

in the Elementary School

Alvin M. Westcott and James A. Smith
State University of New York at Oswego

foreword by E. Paul Torrance
University of Georgia

ALLYN AND BACON, INC., BOSTON

Library of Congress Catalog Card Number 67–10482

PRINTED IN THE UNITED STATES OF AMERICA

to Ginger and Dot

Foreword

Many exciting, potentially powerful, and valid educational ideas have gone unused or have been forgotten altogether because no one has translated them into practical methods, instructional materials, textbooks, and the like. The idea of creative teaching has been among them. Creativity has been a persistent and recurrent issue throughout the history of education. Actually, the idea of creative ways of teaching has never had a very good chance to prove its worth. Teachers and educational leaders have continually struggled to understand the nature of creative functioning, the conditions that facilitate and inhibit creative growth, and the means of rewarding creative achievement. Bit by bit, advances have been made, and in recent years efforts to add to this kind of knowledge through research and experimentation have been accelerated. We need to know a great deal more than we do, but in my opinion we have made enough advances to make possible a more creative kind of education than has been known up to now. This is why imaginative, informed, and hard-working translators and creative synthesizers like Professor James A. Smith and his associates, who have created this series of books on setting the conditions for creative teaching and learning, are such a welcome asset to the educational enterprise.

The task of retooling—inventing and testing methods, creating tests and instructional materials, devising evaluation procedures and creating textbooks and methods of teacher education—for any new educational idea is enormous. It takes tremendous energy, creativity, courage, commitment, and willingness to risk on the part of many people. The inauguration of this series of books on creative teaching is a major venture for Professor Smith, his associates, and Allyn and Bacon. In the past, the adoption of new and improved educational ideas has been retarded by two powerful forces—teacher education institutions and textbook publishers. The case of Braille writing for the blind is an excellent example. Even after Louis Braille had perfected the method of writing that bears his name and had tested it successfully for five years, it was not adopted by schools for the blind.

Opposition came from the training institutions because teachers would have to master this new way of writing and from textbook publishers because they would lose their investments in the enormous embossed books then used by the blind. It was not until many years after Braille's death that his method of writing for the blind was adopted.

Innovations in education are usually hailed as "fads" that will soon be forgotten. This is a common expression of resistance to change. Rarely, however, are valid and worthwhile innovations really forgotten, if they are translated into tested methods and materials. Braille had created an alphabet, a way of writing, that had been taught successfully to blind children. The idea of Braille writing could be rejected but it could not be forgotten. Similar statements might be made about the educational innovations of people like Socrates, Froebel, Montessori, and others. They created and tested methods and materials that have been rejected for a time, but the world has not been able to forget them. Many people have said that the idea of a more creative education is a fad that will pass and soon be forgotten. It *is* possible that creative ways of teaching may be rejected, but they will not be forgotten. Professor Smith and his co-authors in this seven-volume series have in a variety of ways expressed the definition, the spirit, and the truths of creative teaching in a way that will be difficult to forget.

The format of each book of this seven-volume series illustrates concretely many of the most important principles of creative teaching. Through the format and structure of these books, the author and publisher recognize the reader as self-acting and stimulus-seeking. The reader is provided both the guidance and the freedom necessary for creative growth. These books are a rich source of ideas, but this is not their greatest value. The reader who uses them for rapid reading or for occasional reference will miss an important opportunity for personal growth and professional development in creative directions. The "great ideas" quoted at the beginning of chapters are provocative. The suggested activities preceding most chapters provide worthwhile explorations in creativity. The content of the chapters provides a wealth of information that translates research findings into classroom methods and instructional materials. The exercises and questions at the end of each chapter will help the reader to make a creative synthesis of these experiences.

The authors offer themselves as models of creative teaching. They bring to their task the fresh aroma of first-hand experiences in creative teaching in the college and university classroom and in elementary schools. They also offer the reader a variety of other models of creative teaching, making him feel almost as though "he were there." Participation in the experiences of the authors and the teachers they have observed, however, is not enough. The authors have added to this the kind of guidance that helps the reader identify, understand, and generalize the important principles at work in these experiences. This should increase the chances that the reader will develop useful skills and be able to transform his own classroom behavior.

Each of the seven books has its own unique contribution, along with a consistent philosophy. Book I is a creative synthesis of Professor Smith's rich experience in teaching children and teachers of children, a vast amount of research concerning creativity and classroom learning, and his theories of education. It is far more than this, however. The author has gone beyond all of these and, building onto the contributions of others, added his own innovations. He has distilled a great deal of the essence of the creativity of children. Book II, *Creative Teaching of the Language Arts in the Elementary School,* is a comprehensive, well-organized, and rich source of ideas. Book III, *Creative Teaching of Reading and Literature in the Elementary School,* is perhaps my own favorite. It is interesting and exciting and assumes a positive and consistent position on important issues in teaching reading. It will be difficult for the reader to resist becoming a creative reader. The way in which the author heightens expectations and challenges the reader to do things with what he reads is quite compelling. The books on social studies, science, the arts, and mathematics have their own unique features and should be valuable in courses on teaching methods in these areas and to teachers in service who want to become more skilled in setting the conditions for creative learning.

It is my own hope that your creative use of this series of books will help you realize more fully your own dream of helping your pupils live more creatively. This is the challenge of our day. In the past, we have been able to survive with static goals and concepts. This is no longer true. Things are changing so rapidly that our civilization can no longer survive if we insist on thinking and living in static terms and returning to the "old ways."

E. PAUL TORRANCE

University of Georgia

Preface

This is the sixth in a series of books dealing with creative teaching. Each book applies to teaching methodology the basic principles of creativity, as they are understood today through research.

In this book the authors demonstrate that mathematics, like all areas of the curriculum, can be an exciting, meaningful, and challenging subject for children, and that, through the teaching of mathematics, creativity can be developed. The authors have attempted to include fresh new ideas in the hope of making this more than "just another math methods book."

The authors trust that the teacher and the teacher-in-training who read this book will recognize that good teaching is not a mimetic process determined by preconceived ideas, patterns, and methodology dictated by manuals and teachers' guides. It is a creative process—and becomes significant and of vital importance when the teacher brings to it his own innate ideas. The essence of creative teaching is that it must be personal, unique, original, and different. The teacher attains self-realization in a positive direction via the challenge of teaching young human beings creatively. He teaches knowledges, attitudes, values, and skills that will help his students live effectively in their time and place in history.

This book proposes to build attitudes toward the teaching of mathematics rather than develop a handbook of methodology. The ideas here do not constitute a "cook-book" of teaching methodology to be followed step by step. Rather, it is the basic purpose of the authors to illustrate that creative teaching of mathematics stems from creative thinking.

This volume will be most effective when it is read in conjunction with Book I of this series, *Setting Conditions for Creative Teaching in the Elementary School*. Book I explains in more detail the basic concepts and principles of creativity, which are restated simply here in Chapter One. The authors have relied heavily on these basic principles for the selection of the creative material presented in the succeeding chapters. They encourage teachers to try the ideas presented in this book, but not to stop there. It is their hope that teachers will gain enough understanding and security from the principles stated in Chapter One and their translation into action in the succeeding chapters to realize that there is a legitimate place in the mathematics program for their own ideas and that these ideas are worthy of trial. Through the use of their own ideas they will become more creative teachers. They will learn that mathematics is not the isolated language of the mathematician—that it has aesthetic values and is a vital part of each person's life.

Acknowledgment for contributions made to this book must be made in general to the many teachers who provided ideas and assistance relative to the preparation of the manuscript. Specific thanks must be given to Dr. Harold W. Nash, Professor of Elementary Education at the State University College at Oswego, New York, for his advice and editorial assistance relative to the mathematics, and to Dr. John Readling, Professor of Education at State University College at Oswego, New York, for his advice and constant encouragement.

The authors also express gratitude to publishers, editors, and authors for the use of excerpts from their works. Specific acknowledgment is made at appropriate places throughout the book.

ALVIN M. WESTCOTT

1967   JAMES A. SMITH

Contents

I *

Basic Principles of Creative Teaching

The memorize-and-do operations with numbers will not prepare imaginative thinkers for tomorrow's problems.[1]

CLYDE G. CORLE

The Need for Creativity

Creativity has become a precious commodity. That it should be so rare is a tragedy, for all humans are born with creative potential. Life affords some the opportunity to be individualistic, inventive, and creative; but many people have lost their native creative powers. This is due to many factors; they have been discussed in Book I of this series and will be mentioned later in this chapter. The major concern at this moment is the fact that creative giftedness has not been rewarded— nor, in many instances, even recognized—in our schools. And this at a time when the need for creative people has become so great that our survival as a free nation may depend upon our nurturing this gift in our people.

The research of the past ten years has given us many indications of how to foster the creative urge in children. Many myths about creative development have been exploded, and new truths have taken their place. One of these truths is that creativity can be developed in children through *every* area of the curriculum, mathematics included. Another truth is that, in both objectives and behavioral traits, creative teaching differs significantly from other types of teaching.

Part One, Book I, of this series, *Setting Conditions for Creative Teaching in the Elementary School,*[2] reports on research in the area of creativity and explores the nature of creativity. In this chapter we

---

* Roman numeral one.

[1] *Teaching Mathematics in the Elementary School* (New York: The Ronald Press Co., 1964), p. 7.

[2] James A. Smith, *Setting Conditions for Creative Teaching in the Elementary School* (Boston: Allyn and Bacon, Inc., 1966).

1

shall review briefly the principles established in Book I as basic to creative teaching in order to provide a foundation for the material that follows.

Throughout this series a simple definition of creativity is used as a basis of discussion: Creativity is a mental process that involves tapping one's experiences and rearranging them into something new. The rearrangement is new to the individual, though not necessarily new to the world.

Principles of Creative Teaching

1. Divergent thinking processes are stressed in creative teaching. Convergent thinking has been the mental process most emphasized in our schools up to this time. Such thinking involves memorization, seeing relationships, and problem-solving, which narrows the quantity and quality of alternative solutions toward *one* absolute, correct answer. Convergent thinking involves a narrow focusing of one's mental capabilities.

Divergent thinking processes, while not completely opposed to convergent thinking processes, are typified by free association and unrestricted use of mental abilities. In divergent thinking, facts, concepts, understandings, and skills learned through convergent thinking processes are used to form new associations and relationships, resulting in a broader spectrum of possible solutions (answers) to problems. Divergent thinking processes incorporate such qualities as flexibility of thought, originality, fluency of ideas, spontaneity, and uniqueness, and form the essence of creative thinking. Divergent thinking, the key to creative development, can no longer be neglected.

Mathematics teaching in some elementary schools may appear to be concerned primarily with developing convergent thinking processes, for in many mathematics situations one absolute or correct answer is sought. But creativity involves both a process *and* a product. In the *process* of determining how to reach correct answers, students can be encouraged to germinate ingenious, original, individual, and creative ideas.

Creative teaching of mathematics, then, means that both the teacher and the children pose meaningful problems in mathematics and explore a wide variety of methods for solving the problems. Finally, they identify many ways to express the solution or solutions they have selected.

2. Creative teaching results in something new, different, or unique. There are many instances in the teaching of mathematics where many different answers to a problem are acceptable, and several answers may be correct. And quite often the answer is commonplace, but the *process* employed to obtain the answer is new, unique, or different to the individual. In such an instance the *process* may also be classified as a *product*. (In some instances both the process *and* the product are new.)

3. Creative teaching is predicated on the axiom that motivational tensions are a prerequisite to the creative process; the process serves as a tension-relieving agent. The process of creative production has been defined by Marksberry[3] as follows: (1) a period of preparation when the creator becomes involved with and identifies with the problem at hand; (2) a period of incubation when the creator lives with, and is tormented by, the problem; (3) a period of insight when all the parts of the problem become clear and are seen in total relationship, and a period of illumination, inspiration (or discovery) when the ideas or answers seem to come; and (4) a period of verification, elaboration, perfecting, and evaluation when the product is tested for its worth, and tension is relieved.

4. Creative teaching utilizes open-ended situations. Open-endedness in teaching means that children are exposed to problems that challenge them to test many solutions and to put knowledge, understandings, and skills to new uses.

5. In creative teaching, the outcomes are unpredictable. Outcomes designate, in this instance, the thinking *process*. In most instances in the teaching of mathematics, the product (or answer) is, of course, predictable.

6. In creative teaching, conditions are set which make possible preconscious thinking. Among the many theories that explain why some people are highly creative while others show much less overt creative behavior are the ones advanced by Lawrence Kubie[4] and Harold Rugg.[5] Kubie's theory is centered around the idea that as we mature, cultural pressures and the drive for acceptance push many of our experiences into our preconscious mind. The role of the preconscious is to warp creativity. Kubie believes that the creative person is the person who, in some manner, has retained his capacity to use his

[3] Mary Lee Marksberry, *Foundations of Creativity* (New York: Harper & Row, Inc., 1963).

[4] Lawrence S. Kubie, *Neurotic Distortion of the Creative Process* (Lawrence: University of Kansas Press, 1958).

[5] Harold Rugg, *Imagination: An Inquiry into the Sources and Conditions That Stimulate Creativity* (New York: Harper & Row, Inc., 1963).

preconscious functions more freely than others who may potentially be equally gifted. He thinks that both the conscious and the preconscious processes act in such a way as to rigidify the creative processes, and that the essential quality of the creative person lies in his ability to allow preconscious material to readily achieve conscious expression.

Rugg develops the concept that all life is lived on a continuum ranging from the unconscious to the conscious, and that cultural forces drive many of our experiences into the unconscious. The creative act is blocked at both rigid ends of the continuum. Rugg believes that between the conscious and the unconscious there is a threshold over which creative people pass into the "transliminal chamber." In this transliminal chamber the creative mind is free to draw freely from both the conscious and the unconscious, and it is here that creative thought is possible.

In the teaching of mathematics, unreal, untrue, or limiting concepts should be used as agitators to stimulate creative or critical thinking. In order to use all of life's continuum of experiences, children must feel free to probe into former experiences in order to form new associations and relationships which may be applied to solve problems at hand. To make children feel that they *must* follow a specific thought process is to make them feel guilty about testing other thought processes. They may, therefore, push their own efficient, economical thought processes into their subconscious or preconscious and substitute the more awkward, less efficient processes simply to gain status with the teacher.

7. *Creative teaching means that students are encouraged to generate and develop their own ideas.* Creativity as such cannot be taught, but it can be brought to the surface and reinforced by praise or other forms of reward. When a teacher positively reinforces children's behavior that is aimed at finding the answer in a *different* way, he is encouraging creative thinking in problem-solving situations that may come later in time. Differences praised bring forth more differences, uniqueness, and individuality in children.

8. *In creative teaching, the process is as important as the product.* In the teaching of mathematics we are frequently justified in saying that the process is *more* important than the product in developing creative powers in children. The product or answer to the problem has relative value in terms of mathematical accuracy and as a tension-reducing agent.

9. *The effectiveness of creative teaching is predicated upon its*

relationship to the need structure of the learners. Certain conditions are inherent and prepotent in the need structure of every human being. Among those which must be present to cause creativity to bubble forth are physical, intellectual, and social-emotional conditions supportive to the learner's need structure.

Creative teaching is success- rather than failure-oriented. This principle is one psychological condition for creative development that carries a high priority of importance. This is not to say that children should not have failure experiences. It has already been pointed out that children must feel free to try and fail. It *does* mean that they shall not be failures. There is a difference between "failure experiences" and "failure." Failure experiences help children understand the true conditions of life and can help to build character, but failure, especially if repeated often, can result in psychological damage and a lack of motivation to learn. A failure experience may be analyzed, understood, reworked, and resolved; it then may be perceived as a success experience. But failure unresolved creates emotional blocks to learning. "Success-oriented" teaching means that teachers provide opportunities for children to resolve their failure experiences.

10. In creative teaching, skills of constructive criticism are developed. Constructive criticism implies the use of evaluation skills, which are important to the creative teacher and creative children. Marksberry,[6] Guilford,[7] and others have indicated that evaluation and verification are essential parts of the creative process.

11. In creative teaching, ideas and objects are manipulated and explored. In the meaningful teaching of mathematics this principle is of particular importance. Torrance's[8] research shows that there is a high correlation between creative output and the opportunity to manipulate objects and ideas.

12. Creative teaching employs democratic processes. The democratic process can serve to encourage children to engage in self-initiated learning.

13. Creative teaching calls for teachers that are original and intelligent. Teachers should acquire the habit of looking for the variability elements of anything with which they are working.

The work of Getzels and Jackson has shown that there is a high

[6] Mary Lee Marksberry, *op. cit.*

[7] J. P. Guilford, "The Structure of the Intellect," *Psychological Bulletin,* 1956.

[8] E. Paul Torrance, F. B. Baker, and J. E. Bowers, *Explorations in Creative Thinking in the Early School Years* (Minneapolis: Bureau of Educational Research, University of Minnesota, 1959).

correlation between high acts of creativity and intelligence. However, while highly creative persons are highly intelligent, high intelligence has a low correlation to creativity if intelligence is the only
factor used for screening. Intelligence should be one screening variable for the admission of teachers into the profession, but many
other variables should be considered as well.

   *14. In creative teaching, those qualities and traits that are in-
dicative of creative people are stressed.* Highly creative children show
certain traits and characteristics which children evidencing very little
overt creative behavior do not show. (A summary of these traits is
reported in Book I of this series.) The teaching of mathematics is
especially adaptable to developing such traits as spontaneity and
fluency of ideas, originality, evaluative powers, openness to experience, the power to perceive acutely, self-sufficiency, resourcefulness,
independence, individuality, goal-directedness, imaginativeness, and
others.

   *15. In creative teaching, methods are used which are unique to
the development of creativity.* Many methods have been employed by
researchers to *stretch* the creative powers of children and adults. The
work of Sidney Parnes[9] and Alex Osborn[10] is especially notable in
this area.

Basic Principles of Mathematics Programs

A revolution in the teaching of mathematics in the elementary school
has occurred in the past decade. In periodical literature throughout
the country abundant references are made to the "new math." A
decided change in the methodology and content of mathematics programs has been wrought in a relatively short period of time.

   The impetus for this movement, like the interest in creativity,
was in part prompted by the launching of Sputnik. The need for a
sound understanding of mathematical processes in our highly technological society and the need for mathematics as a tool for science became apparent to everyone.

   [9] Sidney J. Parnes, *Instructor's Manual for Semester Course in Creative
Problem Solving* (rev. ed.) (Buffalo: The Creative Education Foundation,
1963).
   [10] Alex Osborn, *Applied Imagination* (3rd ed.) (New York: Charles
Scribner's Sons, 1963).

Increased interest in mathematics brought a flood of new programs for teaching mathematics, and a variety of modifications, additions, and devices were invented to augment existing programs. We are currently interested in The Madison Plan, the Cuisenaire Number-in-Color Plan, the Stanford Project, the Illinois Project, the School Mathematics Study Group Program, and the Greater Cleveland Mathematics Plan.[11]

Many of these programs, and the ideas inherent in them, have met with fine success—if one is willing to accept the criteria for measurement that are applied to them. The effectiveness and justifications of some of the new programs have been challenged and remain to be proven. The introduction of "modern" math in many schools throughout the country has created a great deal of controversy among educators as to the effect such methods and resultant learnings have on the total growth of the elementary school child. One such controversy centers around the advisability of teaching geometry, algebra, and abstract math algorisms to kindergarten children, who have limited experiential backgrounds. It is extremely difficult to compare the effectiveness and utility of the older math programs with the new. More often than not, their primary objectives are different, which makes comparisons very complex. Unfortunately, some school systems have adopted new math programs on the basis of very superficial comparative data.

No one program of mathematics teaching will develop in every child all the mathematical concepts called for by his existing and future needs and abilities. But any plan, to be successful, must be based on general principles of child development and learning as well as on basic principles inherent in mathematics as an academic discipline.

From the writings of mathematicians and educators and from research in the area of mathematics teaching, the authors have selected the following principles as guides for the teaching of mathematics.

1. *Mathematics should be taught in a meaningful manner to children.* Children learn mathematics best when they understand the meanings behind what they learn. Meaningful math implies that, among other things, children understand the language of mathematics and care to know the intrinsic beauty and poetic qualities of mathe-

---

[11] Clyde G. Corle, *Teaching Mathematics in the Elementary School* (New York: The Ronald Press, 1964), pp. 35–56.

matics. Equally important, children need to learn mathematics for use as an intellectual tool and social utility.

Mathematical understandings are an outgrowth of meaningful learning experiences. They are not "rules" to be memorized by children. Understandings usually grow slowly and as a result of many and varied positive reinforcement experiences.

2. *Mathematics should be taught through a structured developmental sequence.* Research indicates that one of the prime reasons for mathematical disability among children in the later grades is a lapse of instruction in the earlier grades. In a modern curriculum, it is recognized that the growth of many concepts in mathematics are a gradual process and take place over a period of years. Understanding of upper-level concepts relies on mastery of earlier concepts.

3. *Meaningful mathematics makes provision for the application of quantitative procedures in social situations both in and out of school.* A practical balance must be achieved between the teaching of basic number facts and processes, and the social applications of mathematics. Motivation to learn mathematics becomes intense when the children identify mathematical problems that arise from a felt need in a social situation.

4. *Sound mathematics teaching incorporates learning experiences that relate to the nature of the learners, including their mental, emotional, and social development.* It is important that children experience success in their work in mathematics. Success sponsors positive attitudes toward mathematics. Attitudes relative to mathematics are as important as computational skill. When poor attitudes are formed, especially from too many failure experiences, children are prompted to build emotional blocks against mathematics.

5. *Modern mathematics programs include a wide variety of carefully selected learning experiences in which number functions directly.*[12] Mathematics skills and computation must be taught in a sequential manner in school each day, probably in a given period. Opportunity should be found to apply the children's learnings to other aspects of the curriculum whenever possible.

6. *Mathematics programs usually emphasize the element of "discovery."* Guided experiences in learning promote progress toward desirable goals. In guided learning, the fact that all children do not learn in the same way or with the same speed is taken into account. Nevertheless, all can be led to discover meanings, facts, and understandings. In problem-solving, the element of discovery tends to make

[12] Foster Grossnickle and Leo Brueckner, *Discovering Meanings in Arithmetic* (New York: John Winston Co., 1959), p. 4.

the learnings more permanent and highly motivational. The mathematics classroom should be regarded by the teacher and children as an exciting discovery laboratory.

7. *Meaningful mathematics programs are built around "problem-solving situations" rather than problem-solving as drill.* Creative problem-solving should serve as the base upon which appropriate computational skills are brought to bear.

8. *In mathematics programs a systematic series of steps are established to make learning progressive and logical to the learner.* All children within a classroom do not receive the same mathematics instruction. In some instances instruction may be on an individual basis.

9. *Mathematics programs provide "practice" for the mastery of facts to be learned rather than "drill."* Practice implies that new skills are put to use at once in situations where they have significance to the learners. The necessary reinforcement for habituation is provided through the application of the new skill to many situations, rather than that application and memorization to one situation which is characteristic of drill.

10. *Sound mathematics programs employ the nomenclature of mathematics so that children learn to use it with understanding.* The processes and operations of mathematics are made more lucid by the language of mathematics when it is properly used. Children learn this nomenclature in meaningful context.

11. *Highly effective mathematics programs involve evaluation as a continuing process in which both teacher and pupil participate.* They include a broad range of educational outcomes and are not limited to tests of computational skill.

12. *In mathematics programs diagnostic procedures are continuously applied in the course of the learning activities so that difficulties will be promptly detected and remediation begun.* This procedure in some instances replaces the general tests given periodically to the total group of children in the classroom.

The authors have described briefly what they consider to be *some* of the major elements of creative teaching and mathematics programs. The reader will identify others as he progresses through this book.

* * *

"What are two and two?" the principal asked one student.

"Two and two are four. Anybody knows that," the child replied.

"Thank you," the principal replied.

He confronted a second child with the same question, "What are two and two?"

"Two and two are four and two times two are four," the second child replied.

"Thank you for the information," the principal replied.

Undaunted, he stopped a third child in the hallway of the school and once again posed the question, "What are two and two?"

"Well that's a confusing question," the child replied. "It depends for one thing on what you're adding. Two jet planes and two oranges don't add up to anything. Two plus two are four and two squared is four but two and two in our base ten system could be twenty-two. I don't know what your question means."

Rudiments: Creativity and Mathematics

It is nothing short of a miracle that modern methods of instruction have not yet entirely strangled the holy curiosity of inquiry.

ALBERT EINSTEIN

The Child—A Stimulus-Seeking Organism

In order to establish valid objectives for teaching mathematics, the teacher has to begin with some basic assumptions about children, about mathematics, and about creativity.

The methods and techniques a teacher employs in attempting to promote creativity in children are somewhat determined by the manner in which the teacher perceives the general nature of the child. The authors' views are congruent with those schools of psychology which see the child as being an active, stimulus-seeking organism; they reject the notion that the normal child is fundamentally passive. But if the teacher of mathematics desires to identify and nurture creative behavior in children, he needs more specific knowledge regarding the nature of the highly creative child.

What constitutes highly creative child behavior in the area of mathematics? This question has not been answered specifically by research. However, Paul Torrance has formulated a general description of the highly creative individual, and from this we can hypothesize a general description of the highly creative individual in mathematics. After studying the list, discuss its implications for mathematics teaching.

I recently surveyed a large number of the studies and compiled the following list of characteristics found in one or more studies to differentiate highly creative persons from less creative ones:

* Hindu-Arabic two.

11

1. Accepts disorder
2. Adventurous
3. Strong affection
4. Altruistic
5. Awareness of others
6. Always baffled by something
7. Attracted to disorder
8. Attracted to mysterious
9. Attempts difficult jobs (sometimes too difficult)
10. Bashful outwardly
11. Constructive in criticism
12. Courageous
13. Deep and conscientious conventions
14. Defies conventions of courtesy
15. Defies conventions of health
16. Desires to excel
17. Determination
18. Differentiated value-hierarchy
19. Discontented
20. Disturbs organization
21. Dominant (not in power sense)
22. Emotional
23. Emotionally sensitive
24. Energetic
25. A fault-finder
26. Doesn't fear being thought "different"
27. Feels whole parade is out of step
28. Full of curiosity
29. Appears haughty and self-satisfied at times
30. Likes solitude
31. Independence in judgment
32. Independent in thinking
33. Individualistic
34. Intuitive
35. Industrious
36. Introversive
37. Keeps unusual hours
38. Lacks business ability
39. Makes mistakes
40. Never bored
41. Nonconforming
42. Not hostile or negativistic
43. Not popular
44. Oddities of habit
45. Persistent
46. Becomes preoccupied with a problem
47. Preference for complex ideas
48. Questioning
49. Radical
50. Receptive to external stimuli
51. Receptive to ideas of others
52. Regresses occasionally
53. Rejection of suppression as a mechanism of impulse control
54. Rejection of repression
55. Reserved
56. Resolute
57. Self-assertive
58. Self-starter
59. Self-aware
60. Self-confident
61. Self-sufficient
62. Sense of destiny
63. Sense of humor
64. Sensitive to beauty
65. Shuns power
66. Sincere
67. Not interested in small details
68. Speculative
69. Spirited in disagreement
70. Strives for distant goals
71. Stubborn
72. Temperamental
73. Tenacious
74. Tender emotions
75. Timid
76. Thorough
77. Unconcerned about power
78. Somewhat uncultured, primitive
79. Unsophisticated, naive
80. Unwilling to accept anything on mere say-so
81. Visionary
82. Versatile
83. Willing to take risks
84. Somewhat withdrawn and quiescent

Most of the empirical studies seeking to determine the personality characteristics of highly creative persons have relied upon traditional personality instruments and life experience inventories. Literature records few attempts to develop personality instruments which might be used either in identifying or guiding the development of creative individuals. My associates and I are now exploring some of the potential uses of the above check list as one such instrument.[1]

Observable Creative Behavior

In dealing with creative thinking as a process and a product, the authors are concerned only with creative behavior that can, in some manner, be observed, measured, and evaluated. This approach is not intended to negate the importance of creative thinking that takes no overt form. The classroom teacher can deal only with creative behavior that takes some observable form. The authors elect to call observable creative behavior *functional creativity;* it is that which manifests itself in some tangible fashion.

Creative Behavior Directly Affected by an Individual's Need Structure

It should be noted here that the growth or humanistic psychologists stress the fact that an individual's behavior is related to his attempts to satisfy certain fundamental needs, sometimes called life forces. A hierarchy (prepotency) of these needs has been identified, beginning with physiological and psychological safety needs, then the need to be loved, followed by the need for prestige or status. Failure to satisfy lower-level needs on the hierarchy eliminates or seriously handicaps the individual's desire to engage in creative behavior except in relation to satisfying the need. For example, an individual who is starving may employ creative behavior in an attempt to satisfy his need for food, but it is unlikely that he will concern himself with creatively satisfying his need for status while his need for food remains unfulfilled.

Primary Functions of the Teaching Act

The authors recognize that the role of the teacher encompasses a complex variety of activities. The most significant activity of the teacher's role is the teaching act, which is aimed at affecting chil-

---

[1] E. Paul Torrance, *Guiding Creative Talent* (Englewood Cliffs, New Jersey: Prentice-Hall, Inc., 1962).

dren's behavior in a predetermined manner. It consists of three primary functions:

1. Identifying and defining valid objectives for pupils' learning.
2. Selecting and implementing activities and materials that are appropriate for achieving the objectives.
3. Testing, evaluating, recording, and communicating children's behavior in terms of the predetermined objectives.

The highly creative teacher of mathematics performs these three functions, as does *any* professionally competent teacher. Classifying a teacher as being high-creative is predicated upon the manner in which he performs these tasks.

Creative Behavior and the Learner's Perception of His Autonomy

An important variable in the promotion of creative thinking in children is the extent and nature of the teacher's role. How much and what kind of teacher involvement in the learning experience is most conducive to promoting creative behavior in children? This question is examined specifically as it relates to step two of the discovery method of teaching discussed in Chapter 7. But the extent to which a learner perceives his autonomy in seeking a solution to a problem directly affects the manner in which he goes about solving the problem.

In creative teaching there is strong involvement in the learning process. There is a kind of coexperiencing even when the teacher seems inactive, and the learner feels this and is guided by it. For one thing, the learner himself may become so involved in his moment of discovery that many important things escape his notice. If the teacher and fellow-learners are coexperiencing, they can then give him the guidance that comes from helping the learner become aware of what he did.

We are dealing with a curvilinear rather than a linear relationship. In other words, with no guidance or structuring by the teacher, little or no learning is likely to occur—even the stimulus-seeking, self-acting organism may not have enough cues to trigger experimental behavior. With a little guidance or structuring learning increases up to a point. After this, there is a decrement in learning because the stimulus-seeking, self-acting organism is overwhelmed, blocked, and disrupted in terms of making creative responses. Other variables, such as a fear of disapproval by the teacher, inhibit the learner from identifying and reacting to learning cues. Some learners, of course, will require more structure or guidance than others in identifying behavioral cues.

The Creative Process and Autonomous Learning

Student learning as related to teacher guidance can be plotted on a continuum with heavy teacher-supported learning situated at one end and autonomous learning at the other. If the continuum has any validity, it appears logical to the authors that there is a negative correlation between nurturing the creative process and heavily teacher-supported learning situations. Uninhibited ideation and creative experimentation grow out of learning situations in which the learner feels free to test the limits.

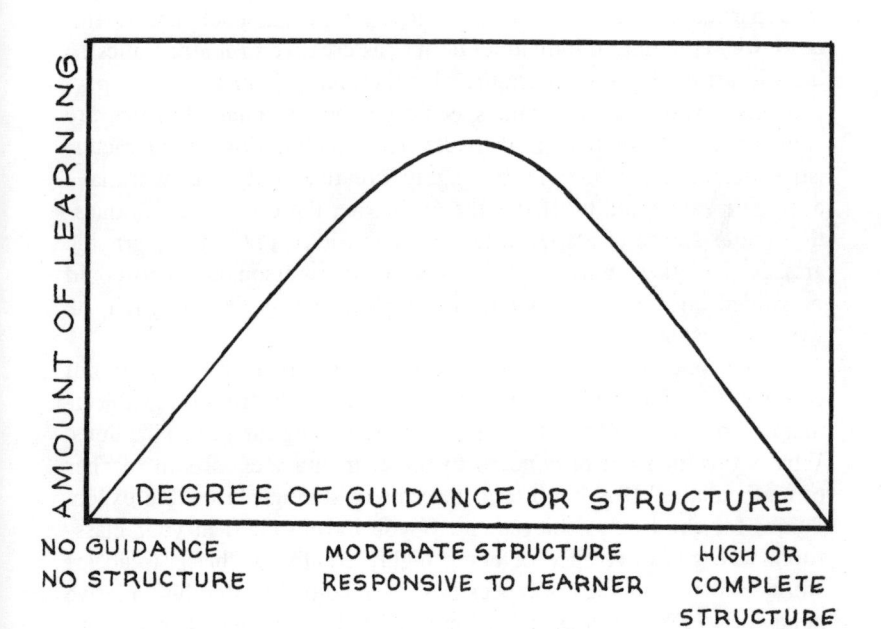

FIGURE 2–1. *Extent of teacher involvement in the lesson*

The lecture method of teaching, which involves massive teacher involvement, may serve as a springboard for the birth of creative ideas in some students, but it has grave limitations. Since the creative process and the creative product necessitate active learner participation, the lecture method of teaching can serve only as a motivating element, not a staging area. In order to utilize the lecture in a creative manner, the learner must then engage in some form of autonomous learning.

Can Creativity Be Transferred from One Area to Another?

Is it a simple matter for people who are highly creative in an area other than mathematics to transfer their creative behavior to mathematics? Many experts in the area of creativity believe the answer to this question is "yes." They point out that creativity can be defined as a particular type of *attitude* relative to problem-solving. If this is so, why couldn't an individual be just as creative in mathematics as he is in art or music or literature? Furthermore, there are many psychologists who point out that specific personality characteristics are common to all creative individuals. The combination of characteristics determines who will be highly creative and who will have average creative ability. If this theory is true, there is reason to question the existence of a special talent for music or one for the graphic arts. Rather, there may be the highly creative personality who could be guided into any area, where, if his interest was keen enough, he would be just as creative.

The fundamental question being raised here is whether or not creative behavior can be transferred (is reciprocal) from one subject-matter area to another. This involves psychological generalizations. Why is this question of concern to the elementary classroom teacher of mathematics? It is important in terms of setting reasonable expectations for children's achievement. If you have a child in your classroom who gives evidence of being highly creative in his graphic art work, is it reasonable to expect him to readily transfer his creative behavior to mathematics if his interest level in mathematics is comparable to his interest in the graphic arts?

The reader should keep in mind that the degree to which two tasks are related would be a variable of major consequence regardless of other factors involved. In the absence of conclusive evidence, it appears logical to the authors that it would be easier for a person who is highly creative in graphic arts to transfer his creative behavior to the area of architecture or photography. After all, these areas are more closely related to graphic arts than are mathematics and literature.

Some psychologists and educators insist that a special talent exists for mathematics, for music, for art, ad infinitum. Some prefer to call this talent an aptitude, but this appears to be semantic rather than academic. The existence of special talent relative to areas such as music, art, literature, etc., would inhibit and in some instances forbid the transfer of a person's creative behavior from one area to another. There are those who say that a talent, like creativity, is nothing more than a special combination of personality characteristics. Others would link particular neuromuscular skills to talent. This would be particularly true as regards the dancer, musician, or painter.

It remains to be demonstrated by research that creative behavior is easily reciprocal (transferable) among different areas. Many authorities feel that the interest factor is the primary determinant. That is, if a person who is highly creative in one area can be "sold" on the challenge and excitement of another one, he will transfer his creative behavior to the new area. Another school of thought stresses the importance of an individual's perception of himself and the similarities between the new task and the old one in predicting ability to transfer creative behavior from one setting to another.

Knowledge of other people's observations and possession of a wide repertory of conceptual models for interpreting his own experiences give the creative thinker the raw material for his solutions of old problems and his discovery of new ones. But without a concept of himself as a problem solver he will not undertake the task of solving problems.

I think it is very likely that a person may be highly creative in one area where his concept of self and of the area permit him to operate freely and may be quite passive in an area where he sees himself as inadequate or unnecessary. But if we are trying to understand the mainsprings of creativity, we should begin by considering the universally creative individual who is concerned with many problems and brings a fresh and realistic point of view to all of them.[2]

There are those who suggest that special physiological adaptations are a part of unusual talent in music or art.

[2] Donald Snygg, "The Fully Functioning Person," *Current Issues in Higher Education* (Washington, D.C.: Association for Higher Education, 1963).

Creative people in different fields may have different personal characteristics. For example, it is commonly believed that the artist, struck by sudden inspiration, must get to his canvas quickly before his feeling vanishes. The special role of the spatial sense and visual imagery in art and of the temporal sense and auditory imagery in music need investigation. Many creative people have stressed the importance of mastering the techniques of expression specific to one's field. Different styles of creating within science have been studied with some success by Gough (1958), suggesting similar possibilities in other areas of creativity.[3]

In his text, *Creativity: Progress and Potential,* Calvin Taylor suggests that the many human factors connected with creative behavior, especially the intellectual ones, are hinged together:

. . . It is likely, therefore, that multiple types of creative talent exist. It is likely also that some of these intellectual components underlie some of the motivational forces in the creative person and are linked significantly to certain personality characteristics as well.[4]

From this statement it appears that a study of the combinations of human factors undergirding creativity, rather than an attempt to point out the existence of a single prime factor, is in order. But, no matter which of these views is correct, the fact remains that a great deal of research indicates that the abilities and/or skills involved can be improved through educational experience, practice, etc.

The Tri-Point Progression

The tri-point progression and the teaching of mathematics begin with the concrete. This rule of thumb for the teacher of mathematics seems more congruous to the roadbuilder or mason. The term *concrete* as used here means the use of three-dimensional materials. In keeping with fundamental principles of learning, mathematics teaching usually proceeds from the use of concrete materials to semiconcrete materials to abstract symbols that represent the concrete. This progression from concrete to semiconcrete to abstract as general procedure for the teaching of mathematics is *not* incompatible with developing creativity in students. It has been tried and proven effective since early man first engaged in learning. If anything, modern mathematics

[3] Calvin W. Taylor, ed., *Creativity: Progress and Potential* (New York: McGraw-Hill, Inc., 1964).
[4] *Ibid.*

textbooks place stronger emphasis on this progression as standard procedure for the teaching of mathematics than did the textbooks of twenty or thirty years ago.

The Tri-Point Progression and Making Mathematics Meaningful to Children

If the reader will take the time to study a few of the modern mathematics textbooks designed for the elementary school, he will find in them a strong emphasis on making mathematics meaningful to children. This emphasis is very old in the annals of mathematics pedagogy for the elementary school; modern math programs have retained much of the proven procedures of the past, which is to their credit. Making mathematics meaningful to children connotes the need to present mathematics to children in such a way that they understand the thinking that lies behind the manipulation of numbers. It means that children can demonstrate with three-dimensional materials the "why" behind a particular mathematical process.

A child can be taught to memorize mathematical principles, such as "Changing the order of the addends does not affect the sum." The same child who has learned this principle strictly on a rote basis might also recognize that these algorisms reflect the principle just stated:

$$9 + 6 + 4 = 19; 6 + 9 + 4 = 19; 4 + 6 + 9 = 19$$

But if a child has learned the principle in a meaningful way, he can, by employing concrete materials, prove to himself and others that the principle holds true. What's more, he can prove it by using a variety of concrete materials—a place value pocket chart, simple counters, or a number line. He can accurately *transfer* his understanding of the basic math principle he has learned into a variety of media and settings.

It is possible to teach children to simply manipulate numbers on paper or at the blackboard without their being aware of what is really implied by the number manipulations.

The Highly Creative Teacher of Mathematics and Making Math Meaningful

The highly creative teacher of mathematics does not differ from the less creative teacher because one makes mathematics meaningful and the other one doesn't. And the separation does not stem from the fact that one employs proven principles for the teaching of mathematics and the other one doesn't. The differentiation has a finer line than that; it lies in the *manner* in which they attack the same teaching task, not whether or not they are attacking it at all. Most mathematics teachers utilize the tri-point progression in presenting new mathematics concepts to children. Assessing highly creative teaching involves appraising the manner and effectiveness with which the teacher is employing either the tri-point progression or some other teaching technique.

Under the Magnifying Glass

Let us examine the tri-point progression as it applies to the teaching of mathematics. Miss Eastburn has as one of her objectives for the mathematics lessons this week introducing her third-grade class to the commutative principle related to multiplication. She begins the first of a series of four mathematics lessons on Monday. Since it is near Valentine's Day, Miss Eastburn elected to have the children use small multicolored paper hearts as counters in today's lesson. The children are excited about receiving the attractive counters. The teacher asks her class to show what 3 groups of 4 hearts look like. Each child works out the grouping problem on his own desk, and many organizational patterns are suggested.

Miss Eastburn has a large flannel board in front of the classroom. As each child suggests a different organizational pattern, he is asked to show it to the class by putting the paper hearts on the flannel board in front of the class. Miss Eastburn asks the entire class to act as "checkers" to see to it that each pattern shown by the children on the flannel board shows 3 groups of 4.

"How many hearts are needed to make four groups of three?" Miss Eastburn asks her class. After an accurate answer has been agreed upon by the class, she proceeds to have her class arrange the heart-shaped counters into 4 groups of 3. Many grouping patterns are suggested by the children.

The class also establishes that 12 hearts are required to construct 3 groups of 4 or 4 groups of 3. Miss Eastburn then poses some other commutational situations: 2 groups of 7 and 7 groups of 2; 8 groups of 6 and 6 groups of 8. The children (at different points in the lesson) recognize that reversing the order of the factors in a multiplication algorism does not affect the size of the product. Both 3 times 4 and 4 times 3 yield the same mathematical product, although the grouping pattern of each is different.

FIGURE 2–2. *Miss Eastburn's counters*

The following day Miss Eastburn presents a reinforcement lesson in support of the first day's introduction to the principle of commutation. Some of the students will need more practice, which they get by using simple counters, while others will demonstrate the principle of commutation on a variety of other concrete materials. These are provided by Miss Eastburn in the "mathematics materials cafeteria" (a corner table in the classroom on which is a wide assortment of mathematics materials). Miss Eastburn alternates her attention between those who still need a great deal of guidance and those who are working independently. Some of the children make a kind of game out of the number of concrete materials upon which they can demonstrate the principle of commutation. They use various types of abaci, number lines, place value charts, colored rods, etc.

At the close of the second day's math lesson, Miss Eastburn observes from the children's work with concrete materials that the majority of them are ready to go on to the second stage of the tri-point progression—the semiconcrete. The semiconcrete materials are usually interpreted as being those which are two-dimensional, such as pictures, diagrams, charts, textbook material, and the like. Miss Eastburn and her students study together the pictorial representations of the law of commutation as it appears in their basic mathematics textbook.

The semiconcrete (two-dimensional) presentation encompasses a third day's mathematics class period, since, in addition to the page shown from the textbook, Miss Eastburn asks her students to draw their own pictorial representations of the principle of commutation using crayons and drawing paper. The students have great fun doing this. At the end of the period the class examines and discusses individual student representations for accuracy and originality. The activity affords many of the students an opportunity to show creative interpretations of the principle of commutation.

The fourth lesson of Miss Eastburn's developmental series for presenting the principle of commutation using the tri-point progression is designed to develop the abstract symbols (numerals and signs) which can express the commutative principle *without* employing concrete or semiconcrete materials. Miss Eastburn and her students "brainstorm" various ways to express the principle using abstract symbols. The children come up with responses like these:

$$3 \times 4 \quad = \quad 4 \times 3$$
$$3(4) \quad = \quad 4(3)$$
$$3(2 + 2) \quad = \quad 2 + 2(3)$$
$$11 \times 100 \quad = \quad 100 \times 11 \text{ (binary)}$$
$$\text{ΛΛΛ} \cdot \text{ΛΛΛΛ} \quad = \quad \text{ΛΛΛΛ} \cdot \text{ΛΛΛ} \qquad \text{(Egyptian)}$$

Then Miss Eastburn drops her real "thought prodder" for the morning. She asks the students to devise some sort of statement that describes the work they have been doing. Soon the students express in their own words the idea that the order of *two* factors in a multiplication situation does not affect the size of the product. In other words, the students have shown that 3×4 and 4×3 yield the same answer quantitatively but that the difference lies in the grouping structure. Four 3's is not the same grouping structure as three 4's. But suppose we are dealing with three factors instead of just two? Does the principle of commutation apply when three factors are involved? For example, does $3 \times 8 \times 4$ yield the same answer as $4 \times 3 \times 8$? Do we change the grouping structure by changing the order of the factors?

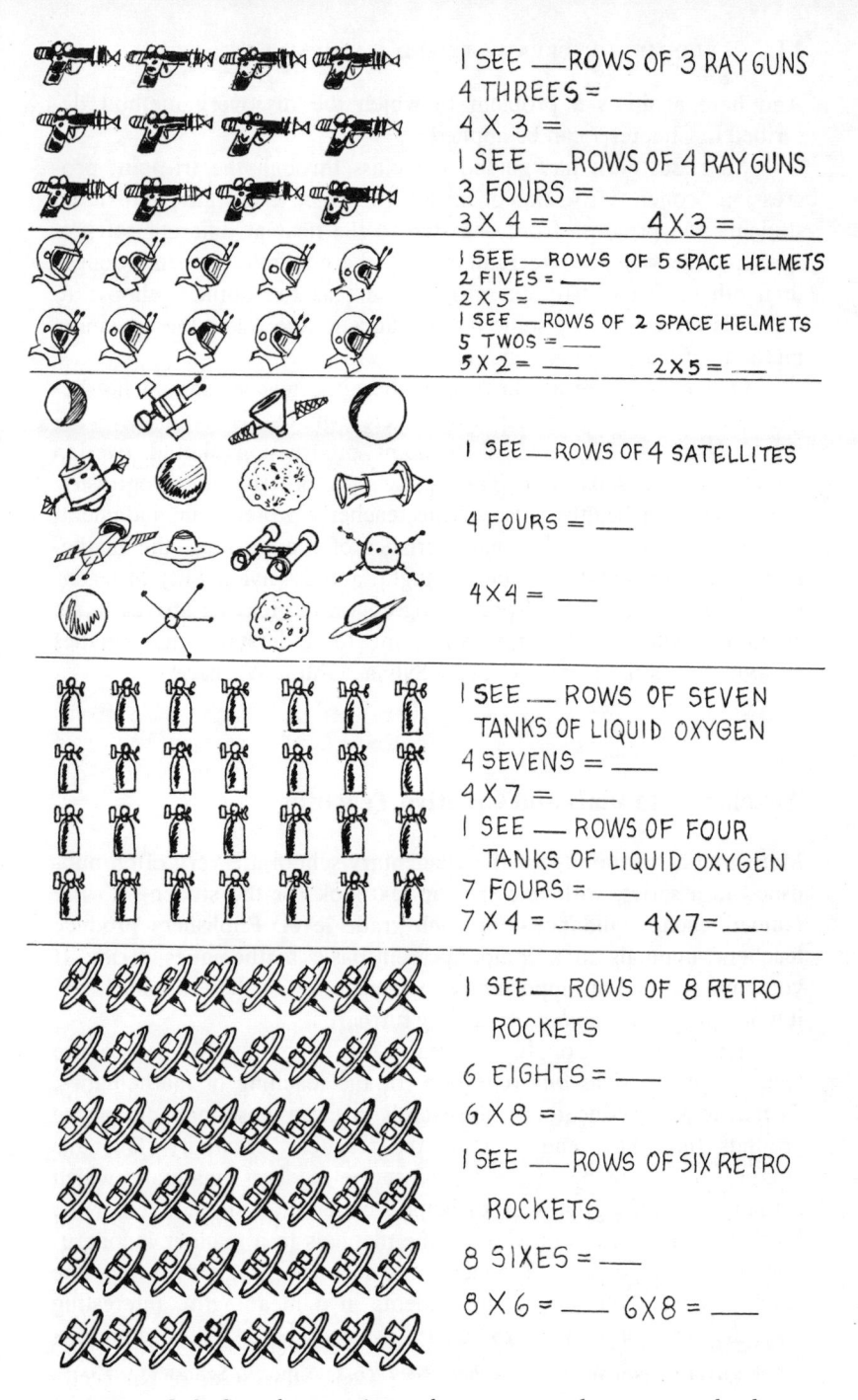

I SEE ___ ROWS OF 3 RAY GUNS
4 THREES = ___
4 X 3 = ___
I SEE ___ ROWS OF 4 RAY GUNS
3 FOURS = ___
3 X 4 = ___   4 X 3 = ___

I SEE ___ ROWS OF 5 SPACE HELMETS
2 FIVES = ___
2 X 5 = ___
I SEE ___ ROWS OF 2 SPACE HELMETS
5 TWOS = ___
5 X 2 = ___   2 X 5 = ___

I SEE ___ ROWS OF 4 SATELLITES

4 FOURS = ___

4 X 4 = ___

I SEE ___ ROWS OF SEVEN
    TANKS OF LIQUID OXYGEN
4 SEVENS = ___
4 X 7 = ___
I SEE ___ ROWS OF FOUR
    TANKS OF LIQUID OXYGEN
7 FOURS = ___
7 X 4 = ___   4 X 7 = ___

I SEE ___ ROWS OF 8 RETRO
    ROCKETS
6 EIGHTS = ___
6 X 8 = ___
I SEE ___ ROWS OF SIX RETRO
    ROCKETS
8 SIXES = ___
8 X 6 = ___   6 X 8 = ___

FIGURE 2–3. *Sample page from elementary mathematics textbook*

And here again is a problem to which the discovery method described in Chapter 7 can be applied.

Miss Eastburn has guided her class through the tri-point progression: concrete to semiconcrete to abstract. Naturally, individual students will progress from one step to the next at different rates of speed; some will need to remain with the concrete materials longer than others. This "tri-point progression," as the authors choose to call it, is referred to by some mathematics textbooks as the "meaning method" of teaching mathematics.

Of course, there are instances where the teacher should not begin mathematics instruction with concrete materials. And there are times when the elements of tri-point progression should overlap rather than be separated. The application of tri-point progression must involve a healthy dose of the teacher's professional judgment; it must be relative to the characteristics of the learners, the mathematical concepts and skills being taught, and the availability of teaching materials. But with tri-point progression the teacher strives to set conditions whereby children will come to understand mathematics *organically,* as the term is used by Sylvia Ashton-Warner.[5]

Teachers' Manuals and Creative Teaching

Mathematics textbooks for the elementary school are very often published in a series, with one specific textbook for the students to use (under teacher guidance) for each grade level. Publishers produce teachers' manuals to accompany their basic mathematics series. If you have not had an opportunity to inspect any of these manuals yet, it would help to do so *before* reading further.

The authors strongly encourage the beginning teacher to use teachers' manuals as *one* reference for the teaching of mathematics. There are many educators who severely criticize these manuals on the grounds that they tend to stifle the teacher's creativity. But this charge should not be directed against the teachers' manuals, which actually contain a great deal of helpful material. It should, rather, be leveled at those teachers who use the manuals in a manner incongruous with their purpose. Teachers' manuals are designed to *help* the teacher present the subject to students in a meaningful, interesting way; they are *not* intended to be used as "cook books." Consequently,

[5] Sylvia Ashton-Warner, *Teacher* (New York: Simon & Schuster, 1963).

the teacher who uses a teacher's manual to help him to teach mathematics is using it in accord with its purpose, but he who seeks to find in it "exactly how to teach mathematics" has a misconception relative to the purpose of teachers' manuals.

Teachers' manuals present *suggestions* to the teacher—suggestions for each lesson, for teaching techniques, for student activities, for methods of testing the students' achievements after each lesson. Both the highly creative and the less creative teacher of mathematics will use a teacher's manual. The difference will lie in the manner in which they use it.

The teacher who desires to inject a large measure of creativity into his teaching uses the teacher's manual as a springboard for developing his own methods of lesson presentation. The manual can be used as a general framework for a lesson; from there the creative teacher may develop his own variations. The highly creative teacher often will "individually brainstorm" various components of the lesson, such as the introduction, visual materials that could be employed, techniques of presentation, etc. For a detailed description of "individual brainstorming" turn to Chapter 7 of this book.

Of course, there are many instances where the highly creative teacher of mathematics will ignore the teacher's manual completely and present a mathematics lesson that is entirely his own conception. But teachers' manuals *can* be helpful to *any* teacher of mathematics; the degree of helpfulness is relative.

To sum up, the existence of teachers' manuals does not stifle creativity; the manner in which they are employed by a teacher can. The teacher who views the manual in terms of "the manual tells me how the lesson should be taught" is surrendering his opportunity to interject his own ideas (creativity) into each lesson. The creative chef does not follow a cook book literally but makes innovations and changes in the standard recipe.

Drill Activities and Modern Mathematics

In order to establish the place of drill activities in a modern mathematics program, we must first determine the educational objectives of these activities. Drill activities, such as those associated with flash cards, promote a stimulus-response (SR) bond between the algorism (stimulus) and correct answer (response). If the correct response to a particular stimulus is given repeatedly, a psychological and neurological bond is formed. Pavlov rang a bell and his dogs salivated in a stimulus and response situation. Similarly, though on a somewhat more complex level, a child learns to respond with a particular immediate verbal response when $12 - 8$ is visually or orally presented to him.

The need to habituate (memorize) the basic facts does not lie within the learner. It resides in the society in which the child must function. If adults had to rely upon counting devices in order to compute simple mathematical algorisms, they would be considerably handicapped. The correct answers to the basic facts of the four mathematical processes have to be automatic—memorized.

Forty or fifty years ago children were made to habituate the basic facts through formal drill techniques consisting primarily of the implementation of flash cards. Often a child's penalty for failing to learn his basic facts was a hard rap on the hand administered by the teacher with a stout wooden stick.

Two Fundamental Differences in Modern Drill Practices

Drill activities have a justifiable place in a program of modern mathematics if they are compatible with the objectives set for the particular lesson being presented. In the past, drill activities were the fundamental and initial method of presenting mathematical algorisms to children. That is, rather than drill activities as a *technique* for habituation, they were the primary method of teaching mathematics. Children memorized mathematical principles and processes on a rote basis. They were afforded no opportunity to discover and/or prove the meaning behind these principles and processes. Drill came first as the *initial* teaching technique and was usually followed by more drill. Often the children learned their basic facts because they were afraid not to. They learned them in a rote, mechanical, superficial manner, and at the same time many of them learned to hate mathematics.

Drill (or "habituation activities" as it is sometimes labelled) in today's mathematics is different from traditionally conceived drill in two distinct ways:

1. *Its placement.* Drill work occurs *after* the basic facts have been presented to children using concrete materials and semiconcrete materials. Drill is of *secondary* importance in the teaching of modern mathematics.
2. *Its variety.* Modern mathematical drill activities are varied in form. Flash cards remain as *one* drill material, but modern teachers employ

a myriad of mathematics games and devices that accomplish the same purposes as flash cards but add variety and interest to the program.

The reader may want to investigate McConnell's[6] classic study of learning second-grade arithmetic by authoritative identification, as it has relevancy to the use of drill activities.

The Role of Drill-Work in a Modern Mathematics Program

There always has been and always will be a need for students of mathematics to habituate (commit to memory) some of the basic combinations of mathematics. The habituation is necessary in order that the learner have the fundamental building blocks at his immediate disposal. Habituating some of the basic mathematical facts can make computation more functional and efficient for the learner.

There is controversy as to the quantity of basic combinations and other fundamentals of mathematics that students need to habituate, although most mathematicians agree that they should include the basic combinations of addition, subtraction, multiplication, and division. But there is wide diversity of opinion among math educators as to *how* the habituation should be accomplished. As explained earlier in this chapter, drill, as traditionally conceived, was largely rote memorization. It involved developing a stimulus-response to the basic combinations with little if any meaning attached. Children were forced to memorize multiplication tables so that they could recite them apart from any meaningful application.

Habituation of the basic combinations can be accomplished without having students engage in boring repetitive oral recitation. The creative teacher of mathematics provides his students with a wide variety of mathematical experiences which promote the necessary process in an interest-provoking and meaningful manner. The habituation activities, however, come *after* the combinations have been presented with concrete and semiconcrete materials. One method of providing activities that will promote in children the habituation of basic number combinations is the use of games specifically designed to help the teacher to accomplish the objectives of the particular math lesson.

Miss Violet Henry, a primary-level teacher, has been leading her math group through a series of math lessons in which the children

---

[6] T. R. McConnell, "Discovery vs. Authoritative Identification in the Learning of Children." *University of Iowa Studies in Education,* 1934.

first "discovered" the basic addition combinations through the use of concrete materials. She then spent several more class periods utilizing various types of pictorial materials, including some basic math textbooks, to reinforce the children's understanding of the basic addition combinations and to help them make the transfer from concrete (three-dimensional) materials. Convinced that all of the students in the math group have a sound understanding of the meanings that lie within the basic addition combinations, she plans for a series of habituation activities.

Miss Henry decides to use a game she calls ADDO. It is played like bingo. Miss Henry gives each student a piece of manila paper upon which sixteen squares have been drawn. Then she writes on the greenboard a list of sums for each letter of the ADDO game. For example, she might write:

A	D	D	O
4	5	7	3
6	7	8	9
8	9	9	13
12	10	11	14
13	14	16	15
15	16	17	18
16	18		
9			4

The children select four of the sums from the *A* column and write each sum under *A* in the squares on their papers. Then each student selects four sums from the next column, writes them in the squares under letter *D,* and repeats this process for the second letter *D* and *O* columns. Each student has then filled up all of the squares on his paper with sums.

Miss Henry acts as the caller for the game of ADDO. The children use pieces of paper, buttons, dried beans, or corn as markers to cover the sums on their papers. She begins the game by calling out, "Under letter *A* the sum of nine plus six." Miss Henry knows that she can call this sum under column *A* because 15 is one of the numbers listed under *A* on the greenboard. The students look under column *A* on their papers to see if they have number 15. If they do, they cover it with a marker.

A myriad of variations can be made in the basic bingo idea to

FIGURE 2–4. *Miss Henry's number games*

produce mathematics games for children. A few variations are shown as insets in Figure 2–4 around the ADDO card. MULTO uses the same basic idea as ADDO except that products instead of sums are used. The caller might begin a game of MULTO by saying, "Under *M* look for the product of three times nine."

NUMBO is another variation that can be used in the upper levels of the elementary school. Instead of using all sums or products as in ADDO or MULTO, NUMBO employs many of the basic mathematical processes.

For the NUMBO card that is shown the caller might call out these algorisms, which correspond to the numbers written under column *N* on the sample NUMBO card shown: "Under *N* look for the answer to XL − X [Roman numerals]; $1 - \frac{1}{8}$; $18 + 1\frac{1}{2}$; 6 take away 8; subtract one dozen from a score; subtract 100 from the number of square inches in a square foot."

Still another variation on the bingo idea is depicted by the ANSO card, also shown in Figure 2–4. In utilizing the ANSO game, the caller gives an *answer* in a manner such as this: "Under column *A* cover any combination of digits which yields an answer of six." A child with the sample ANSO card shown should cover "$11 - 5$."

These games represent one method of making drill more palatable for young children. In other portions of this book you will find other suggestions for drill activities. Some of them may stimulate you to invent variations of your own.

Jane Schrader's Drill Lesson

Jane Schrader is about to present a mathematics lesson to her third-grade class. The major objective of the lesson is to afford her students an opportunity to practice basic multiplication combinations in order to foster habituation. Multiplication algorisms have already been studied by Jane's class in a meaningful manner, and now is the time for the children to habituate the basic multiplication combinations.

Presentation of multiplication tables to a class of children can be very dull and boring, and Jane realizes this fact. The night before, she sat for fifteen or twenty minutes trying to think of as many ways to present the multiplication combinations as she could. She was engaging in a kind of personal brainstorming session relative to teaching methodology. Jane made a list of fifteen different methods and devices she could employ; from this list she chose one to use the next day with her class.

Jane gives the children of her class no advance notice that mathematics is the next topic of the day's work. Instead, she begins by asking the children to close their eyes for a few moments. While their eyes are closed she slips over one of her hands a puppet made from a long green knee sock. He has large button eyes and a mouth that is brilliantly red. "We have a visitor today. Open your eyes and meet Wilfred Worm. Wilfred would like to see how many of the multiplication combinations you know." Jane pretends that Wilfred whispers two factors, such as 7 × 8, in her ear. She repeats aloud to the children what Wilfred said to her, then calls on a child in the class to see if he knows the correct product. Wilfred nods his head violently if the correct product is given. He opens his mouth in astonishment or hides his head if an incorrect one is given.

This procedure continues for ten to fifteen minutes. Then, for variety, Jane alters the method a little—not really a big alteration, but enough to hold pupil interest. Jane announces that Wilfred is tired of playing mathematics that way and wants to change the rules. So saying, she places a small box of cards on her desk. "Wilfred will reach into the box and take a card in his mouth and show it to you. On the card will be a product. When you see the product, raise your hand when you can name some of the factors of the product."

And so the lesson proceeds. Near its close, Jane informs her class that Wilfred is related to a type of worm that takes its name from a commonly used linear measure—the inch worm. While Wilfred does a few gyrations around a cardboard flower placed on Jane's desk, she plays the phonograph record "Inch Worm" for the class. Several other "bug songs" fill out a music period.

Jane Schrader is very unpredictable in her choice of teaching materials, as well as in their implementation. The children in her class would find it difficult, if not impossible, to guess what form tomorrow's math lesson will take.

What teacher behaviors, if any, described in Jane's mathematics lesson constitute creative teaching? Think about this question now and after you have read this book in its entirety.

More Habituation Activities

The types of habituation (drill) activities that can be employed in relation to the four basic processes are limited only by the teacher's imagination and the needs of his students. The teacher and students might want to produce a *tape recording* that vocalizes basic addition combinations with a pause (or silent spot) on the tape for the learner to provide the correct response. Sound effects, such as those derived from rhythm band instruments, could be added for interest to the tape recording. The tape might depict basic addition combinations by utilizing sounds: beep, beep, beep; pause; beep, beep, beep, beep. There is a silent spot on the tape for the listener to supply the answer: $3 + 4 = 7$.

One math group might desire to construct an original filmstrip that asks the observer to supply the sums to basic addition combinations. To prepare the film for the children, purchase a roll of 35mm film from a photographic supplier. Send the *unexposed* film to a processer to be cleared, which can be done by circulating the film through acid fixer or "hypo," as it is sometimes called. The fixer renders the 35mm film transparent and ready for use by the students.

Using flo pens (magic markers), or India ink and small brushes, the children can draw directly on the 35mm film in a wide variety of colors. One by one-and-one-half-inch squares can be marked off to indicate individual frames. It is unnecessary to mark off individual frames on the piece of film, but doing so will give the children an idea of how much film the filmstrip projector will project at one time.

If older children are going to be involved in producing a mathematics film, 16mm film can be used. This can be purchased in any photographic supply store and can be cleared by the same process described for the 35mm film. The 16mm film is very narrow and requires much finer diminutive drawing. However, by drawing numbers on the film in various ways and then running the film through a 16mm projector, the numbers can be made to move—to become animated. Almost any book on cartooning and animation will be of assistance to students in developing some sophistication with the skills necessary to produce a delightful, animated 16mm number film.

Human number squabble (described in Chapter 5), various types of flash cards, programed textbook material, opaque projector, commercially produced phonograph records and filmstrips, etc.—all can help to provide more habituation activities.

Drill is no longer the fundamental method for teaching mathematics, but modified forms of drill activities (which the authors choose to call habituation activities) constitute one important phase of a well-rounded mathematics program. The authors stress here that whenever a child does not know the correct response to a basic number combination during the habituation activities, he should be directed to go back and prove *with concrete materials* the answer he is unable to

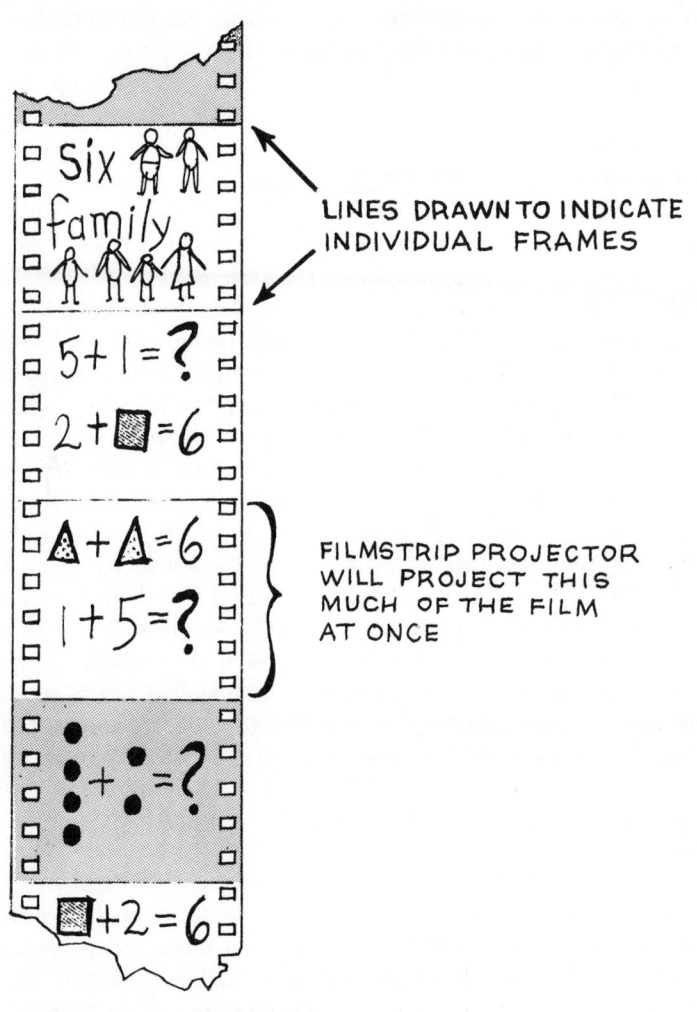

Six 👫 family 👨‍👩‍👧‍👦

LINES DRAWN TO INDICATE INDIVIDUAL FRAMES

$5 + 1 = ?$

$2 + \blacksquare = 6$

$\triangle + \triangle = 6$

$1 + 5 = ?$

FILMSTRIP PROJECTOR WILL PROJECT THIS MUCH OF THE FILM AT ONCE

$\bullet + \bullet = ?$

$\blacksquare + 2 = 6$

CHILDREN CREATE AN ORIGINAL FILMSTRIP BY WRITING DIRECTLY ON 35 mm FILM WITH FLOW PENS OR INK AND BRUSHES

FIGURE 2–5. *Filmstrip used for basic addition*

provide in the abstract. Even flash cards can serve a valuable purpose during the habituation stage of number combinations. But flash cards alone no longer provide the basis for a mathematics program founded upon understanding of number principles.

Stressing the "Action" in Mathematics

Identifying the basic action occurring in mathematical processes can help children to see the relationships between addition and multiplication and between subtraction and division. The emphasis upon the "action" implied in mathematical computation is of great assistance to most children in solving word problems in mathematics. Frequently, after reading a word problem, a child is uncertain whether or not to add, subtract, multiply, or divide to find the answer. Some children will just take a wild guess as to which process to employ. If the child is taught to identify the action called for in the problem, it can be a clue as to which process to use. For instance, if the problem calls for a "putting together" action, the child should recognize that the correct process to use is either multiplication or addition. There are several basic mathematics textbooks for elementary school students currently on the market which stress the identification of the mathematical action as *one* method of attacking a word problem. Naturally, not every child will find this approach best for him, but all children can be justifiably exposed to the idea of "action mathematics."

Two Fundamental Actions Incorporated in the Four Basic Processes of Mathematics

While there are *four* basic mathematical processes which confront students in the elementary school (addition, subtraction, multiplication, and division) there are only *two* "actions" inherent in the four processes. Addition and multiplication involve a "putting together" action, while subtraction and division incorporate a separating or "taking apart" action.

Students can readily identify the "type of action" involved in a word problem or algorism by using concrete materials. The primary-grade student using counters (bottle caps or some other material), when faced with finding the size of the total group (sum) of a series of addends (such as $7 + 4 + 5 = ?$), lays out on his desk each group.

He lays out one group of 7 bottle caps, one group of 4, and one group of 5. To find the total (sum) he *puts all three groups together* and counts to find the number of counters in the large group. He finds that the large group contains 16 counters and that addition involves "putting together" different-size or like-size groups. The teacher may want to re-enact the process on a large flannel board so that the entire class can observe the "putting together" action of addition. Similarly, students in later primary groups can come to know the special type of "putting together" action connoted by the multiplication process. A student using concrete counters (colored toothpicks) interprets on his desk the algorism: $4 \times 13 = ?$ He lays out 4 groups of 13. With guidance and support from his teacher, the student, after laying out many multiplication algorisms with counters, develops the understanding that multiplication involves a "putting together" action employing *like-size groups*. In this case, the size of the group is 13 units (or ones).

Subtraction and division comprise the "taking apart" action. The basic mathematical language used with subtraction bears evidence to this: 9 take away 4; 4 from 9; 9 minus 4. The "taking apart" action of subtraction is not difficult for most children in the early primary grades to identify.

Likewise, the division process when defined as a series of equal subtractions lends itself with ease to demonstration as a "take-apart" action utilizing concrete materials. The partitioning concept of the division process also can be conceived as a "taking apart" action.

In summary, the so-called four basic processes of mathematics actually involve only *two* distinct actions.

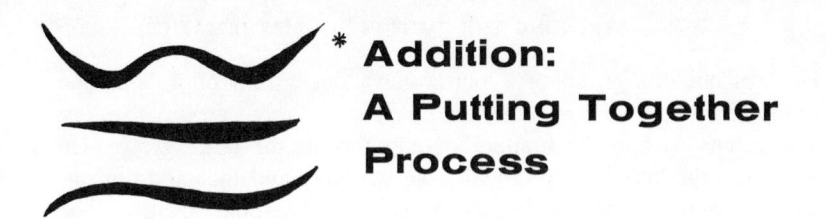

Addition: A Putting Together Process

> *Don't keep forever on the public road, going only where others have gone. Leave the beaten path occasionally and dive into the woods. You will be certain to find something you have never seen before.*
>
> ALEXANDER GRAHAM BELL

Beginning with Addition

Addition is usually the initial mathematical process presented to children in an organized, deliberate fashion in the primary division of the elementary school. Because addition is the first classroom contact that children have with mathematics, and one of the two major "actions" in mathematics, its presentation to children is extremely important in terms of promoting positive· attitudes toward mathematics. The addition process can and should be conceived in a great variety of ways by the teacher and, consequently, by his students. Yet regardless of the modifications that are applied to it, addition involves a "putting together" action. Several parts of a number (addends) are given, and the addition process involves putting together the parts to establish one number (the sum).

When Are Children Ready for Addition of Whole Numbers?

The specific readiness skills that are *absolute* prerequisites to understanding the addition process are debatable. Deductive reasoning indicates that pupils will need the following understandings prior to being exposed to organized instruction in addition:

1. Understand the place value of the digits in a two-place number.
2. Be able to write and read all numerals representing the numbers 0 through 100.

* Three in Chinese.

3. Understand the cardinal and ordinal value of the numbers to 100.
4. Be able to represent numbers with markers in a flexible manner.

Readiness for understanding addition of whole numbers encompasses to some degree the foregoing understandings; it is not affiliated significantly with the chronological age of the learner. There is no specific grade-level designation at which *all* learners are ripe for the presentation of addition of whole numbers. If anything, we have in the past underestimated the intellectual readiness of children to cope with mathematics skills and understandings. *Some* children possess ample readiness for understanding the addition of whole numbers before entering kindergarten. Addition of whole numbers should be presented to small groups of children at staggered intervals so that different children will be exposed to the addition process whenever they give evidence of possessing ample intellectual and social-emotional readiness. Its presentation should be bound to the child's readiness, not to a grade or chronological age-level designation.

Basic Addition Concepts

The first organized addition concepts that are taught to children in relation to addition are the basic addition combinations. These combinations are often called *basic facts* of addition. Again, the question as to whether or not the basic addition combinations are facts, concepts, or understandings is debatable. The authors believe that the basic addition facts are more than basic facts. They are at least basic concepts, and for many children they may be perceived broadly enough to be classified as basic understandings. Admittedly, however, the classification of the basic addition concepts depends upon one's definition of the terms "fact," "concept," and "understanding." The basic addition and multiplication combinations consist of *any two one-place numbers along with their sum or product.*

Since there are ten symbols (numerals) employed in our decimal numeration system, combining each symbol with every other symbol once results in one hundred basic addition combinations and one hundred basic multiplication combinations. For example, $4 + 6 = 10$ and $4 \times 6 = 24$ are basic combinations in addition and multiplication. Many math educators say that there are only *fifty* basic addition combinations because the remaining fifty combinations are simply reversals. To illustrate, one basic addition combination is $7 + 8 = 15$. Its reversal is $8 + 7 = 15$. If a child learns $7 + 8 = 15$, is it a *different* learning task to master $8 + 7 = 15$?

Helping Children Discover the Basic Combinations of the Addition Process

An examination of mathematics teaching methods books currently in print reveals that the basic combinations of addition are suggested as the initial hurdle for children in learning to add whole numbers. Assuming that it is valid to begin instruction in addition of whole numbers with the one hundred basic addition combinations, the next concern is what teaching methods to employ. Here again most of the existing pedagogical texts relative to mathematics agree that the tripoint progression described in detail in Chapter 2 of this book should be used.

Organizing the Basic Addition Combinations for Instruction

Rather than expose children to the basic addition combinations in a haphazard fashion, the conventional approach to addition combinations is for the teacher to organize the basic facts in some manner. When this is done, the theory is that children are better able to see the relationships that exist among the addition combinations.

The basic combinations can be assembled into "families." Here is a 7 family as an example. It includes all of the combinations of two single-digit numbers that have a sum of 7: $0 + 7 = 7$; $7 + 0 = 7$; $1 + 6 = 7$; $6 + 1 = 7$; $3 + 4 = 7$; $4 + 3 = 7$; $2 + 5 = 7$; $5 + 2 = 7$.

Frequently the corresponding subtraction combinations are included in the family grouping. This means that $7 - 2 = 5$; $7 - 1 = 6$; $7 - 4 = 3$; etc., would be a part of the 7 family since they all employ 7 as the minuend.

What basic addition combinations would comprise a 5 family?

The basic addition combinations can also be classified into various sets. For example:

Set I.   The 19 basic addition combinations having zero as one of the addends.
Set II.   The 45 basic addition combinations having sums of 10 or less.
Set III. The 36 basic addition combinations having sums larger than 10.

Would any of these sets intersect? If so, how? The basic addition combinations might be organized in such a manner as to have the same digit as the first addend:

$$2 + 0 = 2 \qquad 2 + 3 = 5 \qquad 2 + 6 = 8 \qquad 2 + 9 = 11$$
$$2 + 1 = 3 \qquad 2 + 4 = 6 \qquad 2 + 7 = 9$$
$$2 + 2 = 4 \qquad 2 + 5 = 7 \qquad 2 + 8 = 10$$

The argument for introducing children to the basic addition combinations in an organized or classified manner is that the learner is prompted by the teacher to identify the similarities and associations among the combinations. For some children the organized presentation of addition combinations in families, sets, groups, etc., may be very important in terms of simplifying the learning tasks and thereby minimizing frustration.

An alternate approach to presenting the addition combinations in an organized manner is to expose primary-level students to the addition combinations in a random, disorganized manner. By supplying the children with concrete counters, such as bottle caps, soda straws, or plastic spoons, they can be encouraged to put together groups of counters and report their results verbally to their classmates.

One child might put 5 counters in one pile and 4 counters in another, then combine the two piles and count the results (sum). The teacher, seeing that the child has discovered a combination to report, asks him to explain verbally what he did. After hearing the child's report of the additive operation, the teacher helps him to compose a number sentence that records the operation: $5 + 4 = 9$. The class is requested to use their counters to check and verify or dispute the accuracy of the answer. Having established that $5 + 4 = 9$ is an accurate addition combination, the teacher then sets the students free again to work independently at their desks in order to discover more addition combinations.

The discovering may take many days, but eventually there will have evolved *from the children* a list of addition combinations that have been discovered and verified for accuracy. The combinations will not be grouped or organized because they have been assembled as they came at random from different members of the class. A portion of the list a primary-level class assembled is shown below:

$$4 + 5 = 9; \quad 6 + 1 = 7; \quad 8 + 3 = 11; \quad 0 + 1 = 1;$$
$$0 + 2 = 2; \quad 0 + 3 = 3; \quad 8 + 5 = 13; \quad 5 + 5 = 10;$$
$$9 + 1 = 10; \quad 7 + 6 = 13; \quad 7 + 3 = 10.$$

One characteristic of the creative process is frequently described as *creating some degree of order out of disorder*. Highly creative children are excited by the challenge of chaos or disorganization; to them it represents an attractive open-endedness. Some children, however, may be threatened and/or severely frustrated by the existence of obvious disorder if they are not supported in varying degrees by the teacher.

When the teacher, or the textbook being employed with the children, presents the addition combinations in a predetermined organized manner, the opportunity for the students to participate in developing *many* ways of organizing the addition combinations has been usurped. But again, for some children a modified open-endedness may be best. To encourage their discovery of the 7 family have them display 7 counters on their desks. Then confront them with a problem that contains modified open-endedness, such as this one: "Using the seven counters on your desk, make as many different groupings of counters as you can. Write a number sentence that expresses each combination that you make."

Addition and More Addition

After the children discover and verify the one hundred basic combinations of addition, they are ready to move ahead to more complex addition experiences. In all addition instances, the teacher sets learning conditions so that the children begin with concrete, manipulative materials, moving on to semiconcrete, then to the abstract.

While learning to record their addition combinations, children should be encouraged to seek *many* ways of recording the basic addition combinations. When this is so, children are apt to develop the understanding that recording mathematical computation is not a rigid, previously patterned task but one that can be accomplished in a myriad of ways. For instance: In how many ways can we express the six plus seven action? Here are a few examples:

$$6 + 7 = 13 \qquad \begin{array}{r} 7 \\ + \, 6 \\ \hline 13 \end{array} \qquad (3 + 3) + (3 + 4) = 13$$

$$\begin{array}{l} 000 \qquad 000 \quad 00000 \\ 000 \text{ and } 00 \ = 0000 \qquad (2 + 2 + 2) + (3 + 2 + 2) = 13 \\ \phantom{000 \text{ and }} 00 \quad 0000 \end{array}$$

And Still More to Add

The basic addition combination yielding the largest sum is $9 + 9 = 18$. Developmentally the next step is to expose children to higher-decade addition algorisms in which one *addend* or more is a two-digit number. Some examples of higher-decade addition are:

14	17	17
+ 5	+ 25	+ 5
Higher decade addition without carrying	Higher decade addition with carrying	Bridging the decade

The phrase "now you see it now you don't" is somewhat appropriate to the behavior of "unseen" numbers in column addition. They can be problematic for some children in their early experiences with column addition. In working the column addition example below, the child who adds "upward" must visualize 11 as an "unseen number." Eleven must be added to 8 in the first column in order to arrive at the correct digit for the ones column in the sum. What unseen number does the child encounter if he is adding downward?

$$
\begin{array}{r}
18 \\
6 \\
+\ 5 \\
\hline
\end{array}
$$

Try to brainstorm some teaching materials, techniques, methods that could be used by a teacher to help children become more proficient in handling unseen numbers in column addition. For example, would it be helpful to a child to cover up with his hand one of the numerals in the ones place? After he added two numerals he could take away his hand and add the third numeral. Does this technique seem valid in terms of the learning task involved?

Addition Upward or Downward?

When computing the sum in column addition, is it better for children to be taught to add from the bottom of the column upward or the top of the column downward? There is no research to prove that adding downward is faster or more accurate than adding upward. The only logical suggestion relative to this problem is that children at the primary levels be taught to add in the direction *opposite* from that in which they are taught to subtract. This may help to stress the fact that addition is the inverse of subtraction. At least it might dispel confusion in the minds of some children in their very early experiences with the two processes. Beyond the early stages of learning addition, children should be encouraged to experiment with many ways of attacking addition. Some inquisitive ones may decide to try adding upward, downward, sideways, and backward.

To promote creative thinking in students, it is highly desirable to encourage them to think about many approaches to any problem that confronts them. This holds true whether the problem is a linoleum block to be carved or an addition problem to be solved. In technical terminology, the teacher assists children to discover the variability elements of the particular medium with which they are working.

In column addition, children are traditionally taught to begin adding in the ones column. After the children have had an opportunity to work at column addition in the traditional manner, these questions can be posed: Do we have to begin adding in the ones column? Can we begin adding in the hundreds column? Would it be easier and/or faster to begin in some other place than the ones place when dealing with a column addition algorism?

Once the foregoing questions are asked, the students should be allowed to experiment with various approaches to column addition algorisms. As the following addition algorisms indicate, it is possible to begin at any place in column addition. The only caution to observe is to be certain that the partial sums are written in terms of their correct place value.

$$
\begin{array}{r} 246 \\ 329 \\ 746 \\ \hline 12 \\ 10 \\ 21 \\ \hline 1321 \end{array}
\qquad
\begin{array}{r} 246 \\ 329 \\ 746 \\ \hline 10 \\ 12 \\ 21 \\ \hline 1321 \end{array}
$$

One child stated that to help himself keep the place value straight in his mind he writes a number sentence incorporating the partial sums. His number sentence for the column addition algorism shown above is: 10 tens + 12 hundreds + 21 ones = 1321. Spirited reactions to his number sentence came from other members of the class, among them several attempts to evaluate the efficiency and general practicality of writing a number sentence instead of lining up each numeral in the partial sums in its correct place.

Variations on the Addition Theme

In any group of students there will be some who are able to learn more rapidly and at a more complex level than their peers. To expose these students to habituation activities after they have demonstrated that they understand and can apply the basic combinations of addition is to waste their time. Too frequently, after a child has completed a series of mathematics tasks correctly, he is given "extra practice" algorisms just because the teacher is at a loss to keep him occupied. There are many alternate types of addition experiences to which the rapid learner can be exposed without having him engage in needless, boring repetition.

While other groups of primary students are working on understanding and habituation of the common addition combinations, children who have accomplished the regular addition hurdles ahead of their peers can be encouraged to explore the addition process more broadly. The following suggestions are only a few of the addition avenues they might explore with some guidance from the teacher.

Using a large mock-up thermometer, a group of the rapid math learners could be introduced to plus and minus numbers (that is, numbers that are less than zero and more than zero). The students could be challenged by a problem such as this: Is it possible to add plus and minus numbers? If so, how do the plus or minus values affect the sum of two addends? We know that $2 + 2 = 4$ but does a plus 2 added to a minus 2 equal 4?

Another area to which the addition process can be projected for use as enrichment material is in transposing to a number base other than 10. It has already been proven many times that primary-level children are capable of understanding the base element of a numeration system. A binary numeration system (base 2) can be used as an initial introduction to different bases for primary-level children. Once the children understand that only two different symbols and place values are used to express *any* number, they are ready to explore with concrete place value devices the mechanics of the binary system. Thus the children can be led to discover the basic addition combinations in the binary system on their own. In the same way a duodecimal numeration system (base 12) can be employed to illustrate similar concepts.

If the children understand that only two symbols can be used in binary numeration, it is a simple matter to present to them the question: In how many *different* ways can the two symbols be added? After some experimentation they should be able to come up with the four basic addition combinations of the binary system:

$$1 + 0 = 1; 0 + 1 = 1; 0 + 0 = 0; 1 + 1 = 10$$

The children may be astounded to discover that these are the *only* possible addition combinations that can occur while adding binary numbers. After they have validated this, they may want to test out subtraction using a binary system. The authors have observed seven-year-olds working avidly and accurately with both addition and subtraction in a binary numeration system. One note of caution: The question raised here is not whether children at the primary level *can* be taught to use binary numerals with understanding. The question is whether they *should* be taught the mechanics of binary numerals. What educational objectives can be accomplished by doing so? Unless justified by sound objectives, teaching binary numeration to young children becomes nothing more than an educational window-dressing.

Modular Addition

The basic addition combinations also can be projected into a modulus number system in such a simple manner that some primary-level children will thrive on them. If the reader is unfamiliar with the mechanics of a modulus number system, refer to Chapter 8.

Using a simple mod 5 clock made from a paper plate, each child in the group can "discover" what happens when simple addition combinations are projected into a circular number system. A set of addition combinations is shown below in which 4 is maintained as one addend. The answers are in terms of mod 5.

0	1	2	3	4	5	6	7	8	9
+4	+4	+4	+4	+4	+4	+4	+4	+4	+4
4	0	1	2	3	4	0	1	2	3

Ancient notation systems can serve as an avenue leading children to discover addition variations. Given only the symbols of the Egyptian, Roman, or Sumerian notation systems, the children can be encouraged to experiment with adding the symbols together. Adding numbers such as 9 and 9 in several ancient notation systems can be a highly exciting and challenging mathematical experience. Is it possible to add Roman numerals in the same manner as we add our Hindu-Arabic numerals? What are the efficiencies and inefficiencies in any of the ancient notation systems? Children can try adding in these ancient systems and thus develop conclusions relative to the strengths and weaknesses of the various ancient systems in the addition process. Then, *to promote creativity,* ask the children what changes they would make in any one of the ancient systems in order to make adding easier.

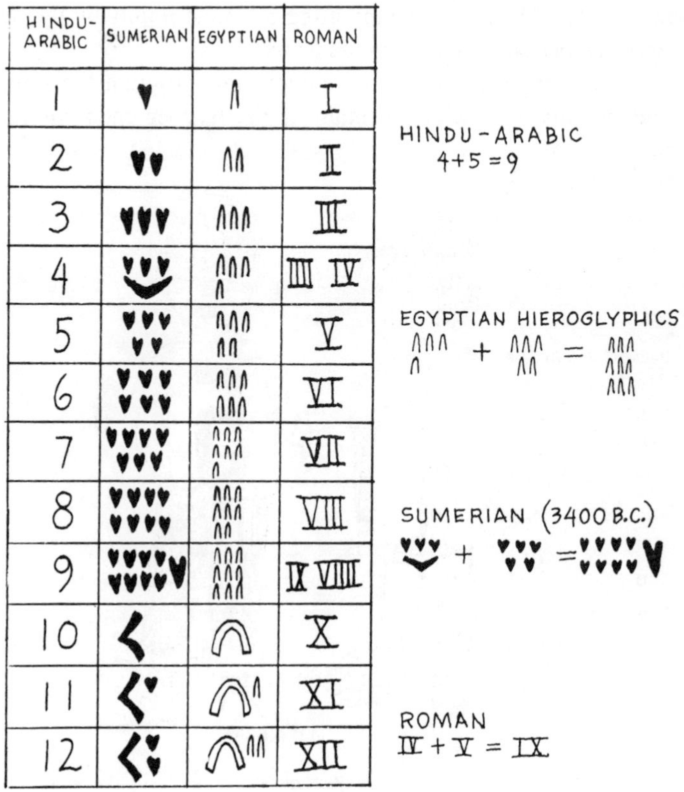

FIGURE 3–1. *Ancient notation systems*

Number Card Game

Mrs. Henry also uses a number card game as another habituation activity relative to the basic addition combinations. The card game can be modified for use with any of the four basic processes, as well as for incorporating the decimal point and percent sign for upper-level use. Mrs. Henry divides her students up into several teams. Each student on each team is issued a large card on which a large numeral is written. The large cards are distributed in such a fashion that each team is able to illustrate all ten basic symbols of our number system (0–9). To begin the game, Mrs. Henry calls out a basic addition combination, such as 8 + 7. Since the sum of 8 plus 7 is 15, the student with the 1 card and the student holding the 5 card *on each team* should hurry to the front of the classroom and form the correct sum as shown in Figure 3–2. The first team to form the correct response wins a point. The team accumulating the most points by the end of a prescribed period of time wins the game.

At the upper levels of the mathematics program the same game could be employed with decimals. If the teacher calls out the com-

FIGURE 3–2. *Miss Henry's number card game*

bination of 26.6 + 15.90, each team must attempt to compute the correct answer. As soon as they arrive at an answer each team attempts to be the first to form the correct answer at the front of the room using the cards. One student on each team has a card with a decimal point on it. In forming the answer the decimal point must be located in the correct position. As the reader can observe in Figure 3–3, it takes five individual cards to depict the answer to the addition of decimals algorism 26.6 + 15.90.

FIGURE 3–3. *Number card game with decimals*

Mathematical Principles in Addition

There are many distinct mathematical principles applicable to the addition action. Children should be guided to discover the common ones, such as: commutative principle: $5 + 4 = 4 + 5$; associative principle: $3 + (4 + 6) = (3 + 4) + 6$; closure: $6 + 5 = 11$; identity-element: $4 + 0 = 4$.

There are two other understandings that need to be appended to the mathematical principles just given. Addition and subtraction can be considered as inverse processes. Therefore, *if one of two addends and their sum are given, subtract the given addend from the sum to find the unknown addend.* In application to the number sentence $n + 8 = 15$ a child who understands the inverse idea will conclude that to find n he needs to subtract 8 from 15. The second understanding is that accuracy in addition and subtraction hinges upon keeping like places in the same columns.

Creative Checks for Addition of Whole Numbers

Children should be encouraged to make suggestions as to how addition algorisms can be checked for accuracy. Naturally, the conventional check of addition (adding in the opposite direction) would be included in the suggestions. To promote flexible thinking in students, the teacher may want to demonstrate one or two unconventional methods of checking addition algorisms. Actually, the suggestion period may be classified as a type of brainstorming activity.

Casting out 9's or 11's may be two checks that the teacher will want to explain. Whenever a check for addition is suggested by a student, the entire math group should be encouraged to validate or invalidate the suggestion. Will the check work? Why does the check work?

Addition can be checked by projecting the algorism into a mod system (see Chapter 8) or another base system. The column addition below is checked in mod 8.

$$
\begin{array}{r r}
 & Mod\ 8 \\
26 & 2 \\
42 & 2 \\
19 & 3 \\
22 & 6 \\
+\ 39 & +\ 7 \\
\hline
148 & 4 \\
\end{array}
$$

$148 = 4$ in mod 8

check

A group of children were attempting to figure out methods of checking addition algorisms. This column addition example was on the greenboard:

$$19$$
$$11$$
$$18$$
$$31$$
$$+\ 42$$

One student suggested breaking the addends up into pairs and adding the pairs to check the algorism. Her written description of her process looked like this:

19	
11	
18	30
31	49
42	42
	121

Lengthy discussion ensued relative to the strengths and weaknesses of the method; there were several suggestions for modifying it.

Another student explained that he could add the column quickly by rounding off the numbers. His written illustration on the greenboard looked like this:

$$19 = 20 - 1$$
$$11 = 10 + 1$$
$$18 = 20 - 2$$
$$31 = 30 + 1$$
$$+\ 42 = 40 + 2$$
$$120 + 1$$

The group, as a result of these suggestions, became excited about the challenge to create checks for addition. For many days afterward, individual students came up to the teacher's desk with checking schemes they had developed.

One boy reported that he had the column addition algorism written on a scrap of paper and looked at it several times a day until he finally evolved a check for addition which involved the use of a constant. An example of his original checking system is shown below:

$$19 \div 2 = \ 9 + 1$$
$$11 \div 2 = \ 5 + 1$$
$$18 \div 2 = \ 9$$
$$31 \div 2 = 15 + 1$$
$$42 \div 2 = 21$$

$$\overline{121} \qquad \overline{59 + 3}$$
$$2 \times 59 = 118 + 3 = 121$$

The children in the class agreed that this method of checking worked, but in general they felt it was inefficient.

Addition Devices and Gadgets

For any one of the four basic mathematical processes children can be encouraged and guided to create devices and gadgets that demonstrate one or more of the processes. Doing this may strengthen a child's understanding of the math process involved as well as stretch his creative thinking abilities.

Some children may need to be exposed to sample gadgets to kindle their motivation to produce gadgets of their own; some may elect to use an existing gadget from which to hitchhike their own modification. Still others, as a result of verbal suggestions from the teacher and peers, may attempt to devise an original gadget or device *without* having seen any existing ones done by other people.

The nomograph shown in Figure 3–4 is a type of number graph which engineers and scientists often use for rapid addition and subtraction. By using a straightedge to connect addends in columns A and C the sum can be read on the center scale (B). Notice the straight dotted line that has been drawn on the nomograph; this connects 16 on the A scale and 30 on the C scale. Now, to find the sum of 16 and 30, simply read the number that is connected by the dotted line on the B scale. The dotted line connects with the marker that indicates 46, therefore $16 + 30 = 46$. To subtract using the nomograph, simply let the B column represent the minuend and column A or C be the subtrahend. The remainder is read on the A or C scale, depending on which one is not being used as the subtrahend.

The subtraction algorism shown by the dotted line can be conceived in two ways. Scale B is the minuend and the dotted line indi-

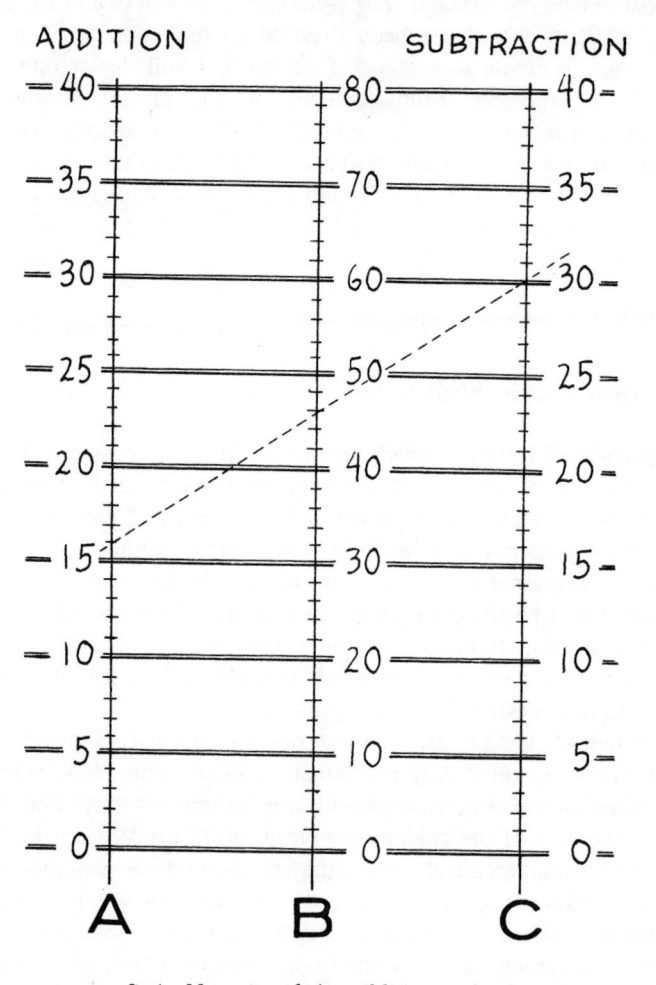

FIGURE 3–4. *Nomograph for addition and subtraction*

cates 46. If scale *C* is the subtrahend (30), to subtract 30 from 46 read the number indicated by the dotted line on scale *A* (16). Therefore 46 − 30 = 16 according to the straight dotted line shown on the nomograph. Reading scale *A* as the subtrahend, the algorism becomes 46 − 16 = 30. Subtraction is accomplished by taking one addend from the sum and leaving the other addend as the remainder. In this respect the inverse relationship between addition and subtraction is neatly portrayed. Why does the nomograph work? Could a nomograph be constructed that would yield products and quotients? Some students who have been exposed to the nomograph may be challenged to create some type of device that will depict one of the four basic processes. Many students in the primary levels have developed various types of number wheels and simple horizontal graphs which serve the same purpose as the nomograph. A boy in the intermediate level of a neighboring elementary school developed a binary and quinary nomograph. The authors suggest the use of more complex nomographs for some children at about the sixth-grade level.

Addition and the Slide Rule

Inexpensive slide rules, which are available from commercial school suppliers, can be introduced to young students as an instrument for calculating. A slide rule is composed of a series of parallel number lines; some students may be challenged to create simple modifications of the conventional one. The slide rule can be introduced in such a fashion that it reinforces certain basic mathematics concepts such as the principle that subtraction is the inverse process of addition. However, to simply present the slide rule to children as a toy or gadget to play with has questionable educational value.

When should children be exposed to materials like the nomograph and slide rule? Any mathematical device should be employed only when its use is congruous with a valid mathematical and educational objective. If the students involved are to profit from the use of a particular mathematical device, they need to possess suitable mathematical background, mental maturity, and appropriate interest. It is difficult to assess any of these elements in one child with any reliable degree of accuracy—to say nothing of assessing a large group's readiness. In many instances it becomes a matter of trying a device because it fits nicely into the objectives for the particular math lesson. The teacher observes the responses of the students in an attempt to appraise the effectiveness of the device. Devices can help children to develop insight into mathematical principles and can be interest-provoking if utilized in a meaningful frame of reference with teacher guidance. Conversely, the same devices can take on the role of meaningless manipulative toys if not wisely employed.

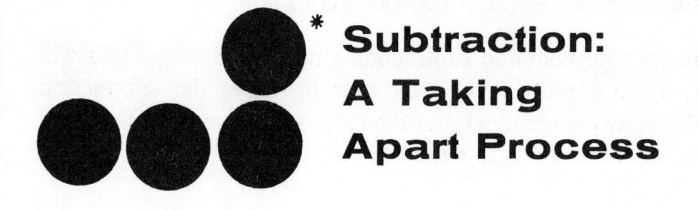

Subtraction: A Taking Apart Process

Before any new order can be defined, the absolute power of the established, the hold upon us of what we know and are, must be broken. New life comes always from outside our world, as we commonly conceive that world.

BREWSTER GHISELIN, *The Creative Process*

Presenting Subtraction to the Child

"When they are getting ready to fire a missile from Cape Kennedy," observed a seven-year-old, "they set an exact time to fire the missile and then the clocks 'take away' seconds until it's time to fire the missile." The "take-away" action can be said to crystalize the meaning of subtraction. Subtraction can be thought of as the inverse of addition. Whereas in addition the child is asked to find the sum, given a number of addends, in subtraction the sum and one addend are known; the child is asked to supply the other addend. "It's like adding backwards," a second-grader remarked. "Inside-out addition," another child called it.

Because subtraction is the inverse of addition it can be presented to children at the same time addition is taught. When children are learning the basic addition facts, the subtraction facts can be integrated with them. For example, when a child learns $7 + 6 = 13$ he can be taught that if one addend (7) is subtracted from the sum (13) the remainder is the other addend—in this case, 6. While it is possible to present both the subtraction and the addition process (action) to young children at the same time, most teachers elect to present each process separately. Subtraction usually is taught after the addition process has been presented. There is no research evidence, however, to prove that subtraction is more difficult for children to understand than addition.

* Four written in Aztec notation.

53

There are four common subtraction situations that children will encounter in word problems. In all four instances the subtraction action (take away) is identical, but the language involved in the word problems is different. The four situations are:

1. How much is left or the remainder.
2. Comparison or difference.
3. How much more than a given amount is needed to equal a particular sum (and what makes—?) or additive idea.
4. Finding the component parts of a total group.

When Are Children Ready to Learn Simple Subtraction?

Research does not prove conclusively that there is a specific mental maturity without which a child could not understand the simple subtraction process. Therefore, the most appropriate placement of the simple subtraction process in terms of a grade level in the elementary school is open to debate. Generally, however, children are systematically taught simple subtraction in early primary groups when a school is employing nongrading, and in first and second grade when the school population is divided into graded groups.

The Basic Facts of Simple Subtraction

Children first encounter subtraction in an organized manner via a presentation of the basic subtraction combinations. One organizational pattern that teachers employ is to present to the children basic combinations (facts) that have a common subtrahend, such as the number 1. The basic combinations for subtracting by 1 are as follows:

$$\begin{array}{rrrrrrrrrr}
1 & 2 & 3 & 4 & 5 & 6 & 7 & 8 & 9 & 10 \\
-1 & -1 & -1 & -1 & -1 & -1 & -1 & -1 & -1 & -1 \\
\hline
0 & 1 & 2 & 3 & 4 & 5 & 6 & 7 & 8 & 9
\end{array}$$

Notice that $0 - 1$ is not used, as it yields a negative number. The basic combinations that employ 1 as the subtrahend stop at $10 - 1 = 9$. The combination $11 - 1 = 10$ is not considered a basic fact, because, to subtract 1 from 11 using written symbols, a child needs to know how to subtract 1 from 1, and this has already been presented.

Another plan for presenting the basic facts of subtraction to children is to group the basic facts according to families. The 4 family (set) in subtraction is traditionally conceived as follows:

4	5	6	7	8	9	10	11	12	13
− 0	− 1	− 2	− 3	− 4	− 5	− 6	− 7	− 8	− 9
4	4	4	4	4	4	4	4	4	4

This represents all the subtraction algorisms that utilize a single-digit subtrahend and result in 4 as the remainder. What algorisms would comprise the 5, 6, and 7 families? Even though subtraction may be presented to the children at a later time than addition, it is important for the teacher to lead children to *discover* the relationships between the two processes. For example, a simple relationship between the two processes can be illustrated in this fashion:

$$\begin{array}{ll} 9 & \text{addend} \\ + 8 & \text{addend} \\ \hline 17 & \text{sum} \end{array} \qquad \begin{array}{ll} 17 & \text{sum} \\ - 8 & \text{addend} \\ \hline 9 & \text{addend} \end{array}$$

The initial teaching of subtraction to most children should involve the tri-point progression. The mathematics teacher introduces the process to children by using concrete materials for instruction. The concrete materials give way to semiconcrete ones, and finally the process is represented by written symbols. This progression will enable children to understand the meaning of the subtraction action rather than to simply acquire the skill to manipulate numerals.

Initial teaching of subtraction is based upon concrete materials! To understand the "action" of the subtraction process children at the primary levels of the elementary school should subtract using three-dimensional (concrete) materials.

* * *

Mrs. Ladd, a teacher in the primary division of a nongraded school, introduces the subtraction process to a portion of her students by employing a word problem derived from the students' environment. This morning on the playground, Jimmy, Alice, Fred, Julie, and Shirley were climbing on the magic carpet (a piece of playground equipment designed for climbing). After a short time Jimmy and Fred decided they would rather play kick ball, and so they left the magic carpet. How many children were left on the magic carpet?

Mrs. Ladd requests that the five children mentioned in the word problem "act out" the problem in front of their classmates. The class counts how many children are left. There were five children on the magic carpet; two left and three remain. Mrs. Ladd helps the class to record their thinking. First she uses the drawing shown in Figure 4–1. Next Mrs. Ladd asks the children to prove, using their counters, that "five take away two leaves three." At their tables the children lay out five counters consisting of dried beans, milk bottle caps, soda straws, etc., and take away two counters. They *see* and *feel* the take-away process. Utilizing these three-dimensional counters constitutes the concrete materials stage of the tri-point progression.

After the children prove with counters that five take away two leaves three, Mrs. Ladd explains that there are many ways that their action can be recorded. By writing "5 − 2 leaves 3" the class can shorten its original number sentence "five take away two equals

5 TAKE AWAY 2 LEAVES [   ]

FIGURE 4–1. *Acting out the word problem*

three." The minus sign replaces the words "take away." Using their counters to prove and check the answers, the children, with Mrs. Ladd's guidance, develop the entire set of subtraction combinations that have 2 as the subtrahend and which result in a positive whole number from 0 through 9. The set is:

$$
\begin{array}{cccccccccc}
2 & 3 & 4 & 5 & 6 & 7 & 8 & 9 & 10 & 11 \\
-2 & -2 & -2 & -2 & -2 & -2 & -2 & -2 & -2 & -2 \\
\end{array}
$$

The set does not include $12 - 2$ or $13 - 2$, as these combinations involve repetition. If a child can subtract 2 from 2, he should have no difficulty subtracting 12 from 2, if he sees the relationship between the two examples.

Mrs. Ladd discusses with the children why 1 minus 2 and 0 minus 2 are not a part of the set (*they result in a remainder that is a negative number*). She uses the expression "in the hole" to explain the negative number idea since most children are familiar with the phrase from some of their games.

For the next day's lesson Mrs. Ladd chooses to reinforce the children's understanding of the subtraction action by employing concrete materials. The night before, Mrs. Ladd individually brainstormed a large number of materials and methods she might use to review the subtraction set that utilizes 2 as the subtrahend and whose remainders are not greater than 9. She finally decided to utilize a flannel board and some cutouts with spring as a theme.

The lesson opens with Mrs. Ladd calling the attention of the children to some of the wonderful "feelings" of spring. She does not announce that a mathematics lesson is in the making, but asks the children if any of them have ever seen a black-eyed Susan. A child identifies it as a wild flower.

"Well, I have brought a special black-eyed Susan with me this afternoon. I wonder if any of you thought of a black-eyed Susan like this?" Mrs. Ladd displays a cardboard cutout of a girl with a black eye. "This is not the kind of black-eyed Susan we will be working with this afternoon. But if this little girl's name is Susan then she is a black-eyed Susan, isn't she?"

She continues by explaining that they must not play near the swings on the playground, or one of them might end up a black-eyed Susan if struck by a swing. This deliberate playground safety interjection taken care of, Mrs. Ladd displays the large cardboard black-eyed Susan she has on her flannel board.

FIGURE 4–2. *Black-eyed Susan*

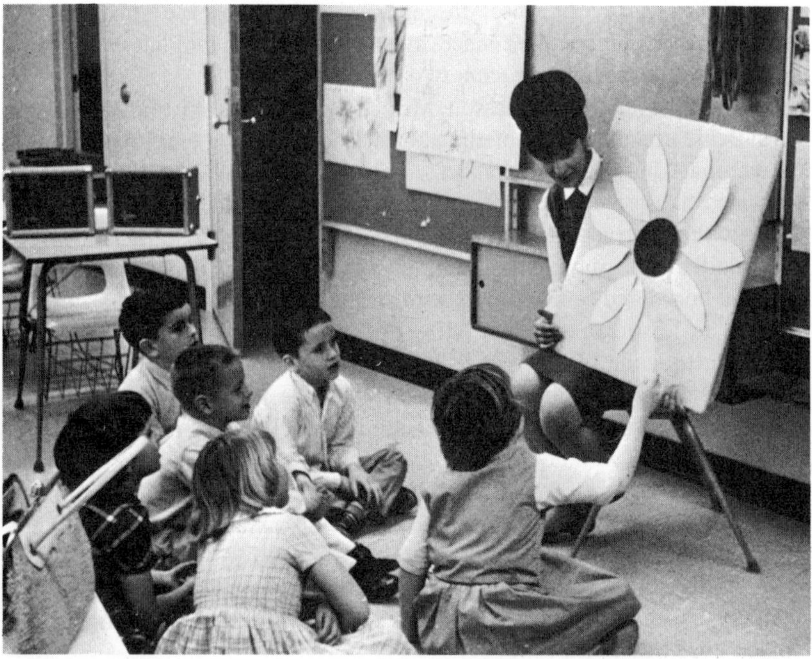

FIGURE 4–3. *The other black-eyed Susan*

She has decided in her lesson plan to use direct questioning as the basic method for reviewing subtraction by 2's with the students. Her method is a modified version of a Socratic teaching method.

"What are these parts of the flower called?" "How many petals do you see?" "If Jean comes up and picks off two of the petals how many petals will be left?" Does Mrs. Ladd's use of the large cardboard flower with "pull-off" petals constitute creative teaching?

Mrs. Ladd provides little information for the children, but they prove each answer by counting the petals. For this portion of the lesson Mrs. Ladd's verbalisms are of this nature: How do you know that answer is correct? Why? How? How can you prove that? If we took two more away how many are left? Does anyone want to challenge Bob's answer? Has Alice counted the remainder correctly?

In this early subtraction experience for the children, Mrs. Ladd is deliberately consistent in the "subtraction language" that she employs with the children. She uses "take away," "original number," "what is left," "number to be subtracted," and "remainder" as basic terminology. It is helpful to early learning if the teacher consistently utilizes specific terms to mean specific elements of the subtraction action. Introducing a variety of subtraction terms *before* a child understands the basic subtraction process may serve to confuse the young child.

Later on Mrs. Ladd will deliberately expose children to a host of subtraction terms, as this will aid many children to develop an understanding of the variability elements of the subtraction process. She will use such terms as "what is left," "how many more," "difference," and the like.

After the children pick off the petals by twos from Mrs. Ladd's flannel board flower, she introduces work to be done individually. Here each child will find an opportunity to prove to himself any of the subtraction-by-two basic facts he still has doubt about.

Mrs. Ladd passes fifteen or more rabbits, simply made from colored paper, to each student at his table. In addition to the colored paper rabbits, each student is given one large sheet of colored paper, which is to serve as the rabbit "hutch." Each student is encouraged to place his paper rabbits on the paper hutch in some manner of his own choosing. Mrs. Ladd then requests the children in this particular math group to prove by counting rabbits the answer to each of the basic subtraction algorisms she has written on the chalkboard. On the board the subtraction algorisms are written both horizontally and vertically:

$$11 - 2 \text{ leaves } (?) \qquad \begin{array}{r} 8 \\ -2 \\ \hline ? \end{array}$$

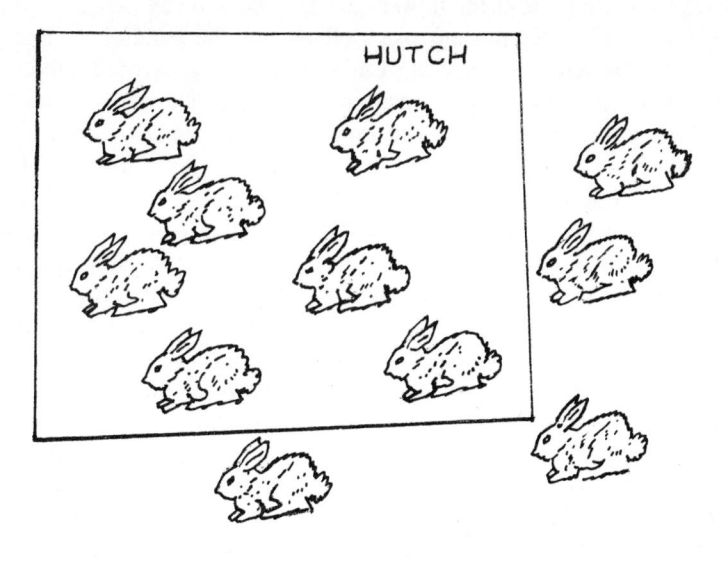

FIGURE 4–4. *The rabbit hutch*

If a child is uncertain of a remainder, he can reinforce the correct remainder in his mind by subtracting rabbits from the hutch to find the remainder. Does the implementation of the rabbit hutch idea by Mrs. Ladd constitute creative teaching in any of its aspects?

When Mrs. Ladd believes that a student has developed a sound understanding of the subtraction action, using two as the subtrahend, she encourages him to proceed to specific pages in the mathematics basic textbook. The textbook work *follows* the use of concrete materials and understanding of the basic combinations. On the specified pages of the textbook the children find pictorial representations of the subtraction-by-twos action. The pictures in the textbook are two-dimensional and represent the *semiconcrete* approach to the subtraction action being taught. Mrs. Ladd may want to supplement the pictorial representation of the subtraction action by using a modified type of flash cards which she constructed for the lesson. These have pictorial representations of the process or processes on one side and various ways of symbolizing the subtraction (and addition) process on the back.

Mrs. Ladd on succeeding days will help her students to discover the remainder of the basic subtraction facts. You may recall from the discussion of addition of whole numbers that a basic fact is *any two one-place numbers together with their sum.* For example, $4 + 6 = 10$ and $5 + 8 = 13$. Each basic combination in addition has a corresponding one in subtraction; thus $6 + 5 = 11$ corresponds to $11 - 5 = 6$. The basic subtraction facts conclude with $18 - 9 = 9$. From that point on all other subtraction situations repeat previously learned facts.

One of the primary problems Mrs. Ladd faces in helping her class to discover the basic facts of subtraction is maintaining a high interest level in her students. No matter what area of mathematics is being taught, student interest and enthusiasm can be kept high by employing a wide variety of creative teaching aids. The aids alone will not hold interest levels high, but when they are used in a dynamic, even dramatic, manner they are effective in promoting both interest and better understanding of the mathematical process being taught. Mrs. Ladd realizes that concrete materials could be used with children in such a restrictive manner as to tie down children's thinking with the devices. Open-ended problems need to be coupled with the concrete materials so that children can explore many solutions to a problem as well as many methods for finding the solutions.

When Mrs. Ladd was guiding various mathematics groups through subtraction by threes, she employed a large giraffe cut out of a poster board. The children "subtracted spots" from the giraffe by threes and recorded the remainder. Mrs. Ladd asked them to be "spot removers" that day.

When the class was working on subtracting by nine, Mrs. Ladd introduced the children to the use of a number line. Under Mrs. Ladd's guidance the class painted a large number line on the blacktop portion of the school playground as far as they could extend it. Then different students took turns walking along the number line in order to pace off subtraction algorisms. Does this activity imply creative teaching behavior? For example, in demonstrating the algorism $15 - 9$ a child walked back 9 notches from 15 on the number line, which placed the student at the 6th notch of the number line.

Mrs. Ladd also encouraged the children to demonstrate some of the basic facts of addition they already had learned. The children soon realized that addition on the number line involved walking "forward" while subtraction involved walking "backward" (toward zero). One child astutely commented that subtraction must be the reverse of addition.

The number line, the giraffe, the black-eyed Susan, the rabbits

GIRAFFE CUT OUT OF STIFF CARDBOARD

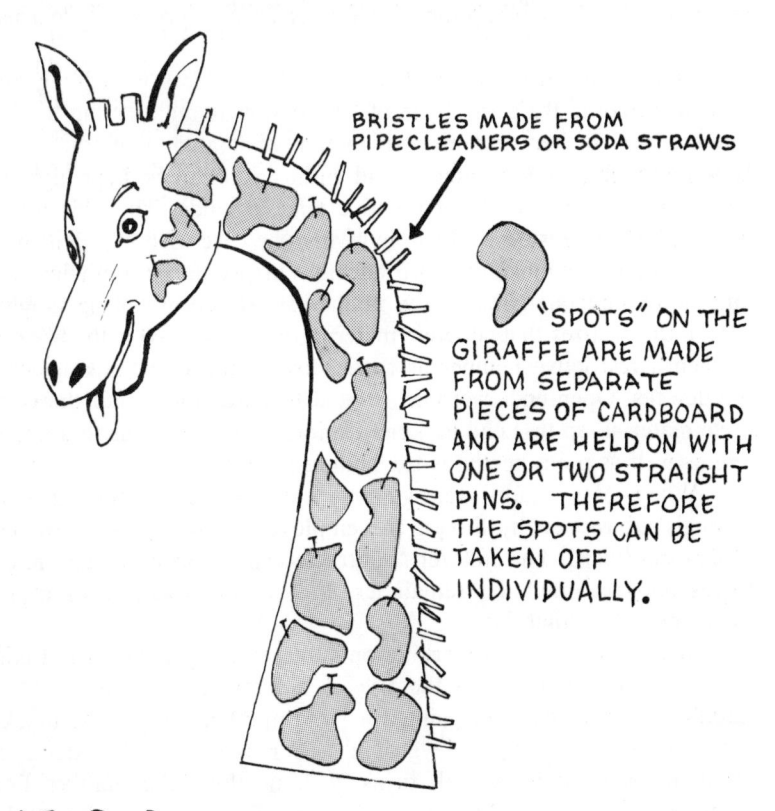

BRISTLES MADE FROM
PIPECLEANERS OR SODA STRAWS

"SPOTS" ON THE
GIRAFFE ARE MADE
FROM SEPARATE
PIECES OF CARDBOARD
AND ARE HELD ON WITH
ONE OR TWO STRAIGHT
PINS. THEREFORE
THE SPOTS CAN BE
TAKEN OFF
INDIVIDUALLY.

NEEDED: SOME YOUNG SPOT REMOVERS

FIGURE 4–5. *Cardboard giraffe*

are but a few of the creative materials which Mrs. Ladd employs to make the discovery of basic combinations (facts) more stimulating and meaningful to children. As the children of Mrs. Ladd's class discover the various basic combinations related to the subtraction process, they record on chart paper the results of their discoveries. Eventually they will have discovered the 100 basic facts of subtraction.

Bigger and More Complex "Take Away"

After children have had discovery and habituation experiences with the basic facts of subtraction, they can proceed to a more complex step. In the four fundamental processes of mathematics it is not difficult to identify developmental steps of varying complexities *within* each process. Because this is so, mathematics is said to possess an *internal logic*. Learning one step or process in mathematics may be a prerequisite to or may preclude the learning of another one. For example, a learner must know how to subtract and multiply before he can be taught some types of division actions using whole numbers, since the division process utilizes subtraction and multiplication. In subtraction, as with the other three basic processes, there are some rather obvious internal developmental steps that can be identified. Simply stated, there are types of subtraction algorisms which obviously are more complex than others and therefore present a more advanced mental challenge to the learner than other subtraction algorisms. Once the varying complexities of subtraction are identified, it is relatively simple to set up a developmental series of subtraction tasks. In fact, most of the basic mathematics textbooks designed for use in the elementary school are organized in a developmental manner.

Simple and Compound Subtraction

Compound subtraction includes those subtraction examples in which it is necessary to regroup the larger number in order to subtract. An example of compound subtraction can be seen below:

$$\begin{array}{r} 33 \\ -\ 18 \\ \hline \end{array}$$

There are three well-known methods of subtraction which may be applied to the compound subtraction situation: the decomposition method, the additive method, and the equal-additions method. The reader will find a representation of the three methods of subtraction that can be employed when regrouping is necessary in Figure 4–6. There are four rectangles rather than three to describe the three methods, since the additive method may be conceived in two ways. In

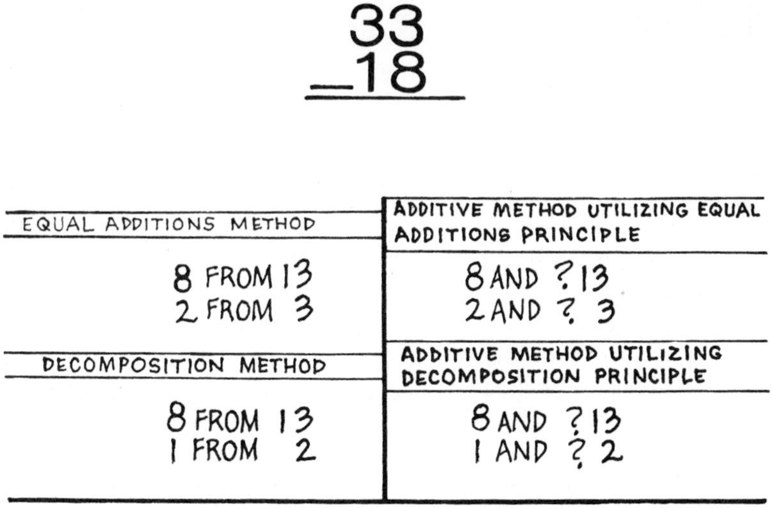

$$\begin{array}{r} 33 \\ -18 \\ \hline \end{array}$$

EQUAL ADDITIONS METHOD	ADDITIVE METHOD UTILIZING EQUAL ADDITIONS PRINCIPLE
8 FROM 13 2 FROM 3	8 AND ? 13 2 AND ? 3
DECOMPOSITION METHOD	ADDITIVE METHOD UTILIZING DECOMPOSITION PRINCIPLE
8 FROM 13 1 FROM 2	8 AND ? 13 1 AND ? 2

FIGURE 4–6. *Three ways of subtracting with one algorism*

each rectangle you will find numerals and words that a child might "say to himself" in using that particular method of subtraction.

To teach children the "action of regrouping" in compound subtraction, teaching aids should be employed which permit the learners to actually regroup numbers utilizing place value. Most abaci as well as place-value pocket charts or boxes are well suited to the task. A number line can also be of some assistance in explaining certain aspects of compound subtraction.

The Big Three, Take Away One

Which of the three methods of subtraction should you teach to your students? Actually the answer to this question is rather simple. To save confusion in the minds of some young students it is generally agreed by math educators that the young child should be taught *one* method for working a compound subtraction algorism or word problem. After the student *understands* one method of subtraction, it is highly desirable to expose him to several others in the interest of developing flexible thinking. There are many, many ways to think about a subtraction situation. After experiencing methods of subtraction other than the one he learned initially, a child may adopt one of the other methods as being the best for him.

The additive method of subtraction has dropped out of usage as the primary or initial method of teaching children to work compound subtraction algorisms. This method, also known as the Austrian method, enjoyed rather wide popularity in this country in the 1920's and 1930's. Its advocates cited the bond that could be established between addition and subtraction; the *two* processes could be taught as a unified process, thus saving time. If a child was taught that $6 + 3 = 9$, he could at the same time form a bond among the other combinations of 6 and 9: $3 + 6 = 9$; $6 + ? = 9$; and $3 + ? = 9$. In the last two examples the child subtracts to find the answer, but the example is treated like an addition situation. The additive method of subtraction treats addition and subtraction as being the same action. In contrast, most modern math programs stress that addition and subtraction are the inverse of each other.

Children should not be exposed to the additive method of subtraction until after they have learned one of the other two methods of subtraction. The additive method, when shown on a number line, appears to be an addition situation, yet subtraction is used to find the answer. An example of this appears in this simple word problem: Mike Nichols is collecting "Smoothie" soft-drink bottle caps. When Mike has collected 10 bottle caps he can exchange the caps for an outer-space decoder ring. Mike has collected 6 bottle caps. How many more does he need to obtain the ring?

The problem is really asking this question: How many bottle caps does Mike have to add to the 6 he already has in order to have 10? As a number sentence the word problem could be written like this: $6 + ? = 10$. On the number line it means this: Mike is at 6; how many notches does he need to move in order to reach 10?

The additive method of subtraction asks the problem-solver to *find how much more than a given amount is required to equal a given sum*. Since this emphasizes the addition process and does not point up addition and subtraction as opposite processes, it should not be used as the *initial* method of teaching subtraction to children.

Behind the Scenes

Both the decomposition method and the equal additions method of compound subtraction have one or more mathematical bases that can be understood by very young children when concrete materials are employed to explain the processes. Preferably, the teaching aids should be such as to enable the teacher and students to indicate place value. Suggestions for creating teaching devices that illustrate place value can be found in Chapter 11.

The basic mathematics principle undergirding the decomposition method is that any number can be regrouped or decomposed. If the children have previously learned this principle, teaching them to attack compound subtraction is a much easier task. Most modern math programs devote time to teaching children to "express numbers in different forms." This not only promotes a flexible concept of numbers in the minds of children, it is also readiness work for understanding compound subtraction.

If students have not had experience in decomposing numbers, then it will be necessary to spend some time helping them to understand this process. The number 13, for example, can be decomposed in a host of ways: $13 = (9 + 4)$; $13 = (10 + 3)$; $13 = (6 + 7)$; $13 = (6\frac{1}{2} + ?)$; $13 = \boxed{?} + \boxed{?} + 5$. Once the student realizes that any number but zero can be decomposed, he is ready to understand the mechanics of the decomposition method of subtraction. Using the decomposition method on the algorism $33 - 18$ shown earlier in this chapter, the child is introduced to the fact that as the algorism stands he cannot subtract in the ones column. He cannot subtract 8 ones from 3 ones. Where can he go to get more ones? If he decomposes the 33 into 2 tens and 13 ones, he can subtract. Using a pocket place-value chart to show this decomposition it goes as follows:

First show the number which you have—the minuend 33 (see Figure 4–7).

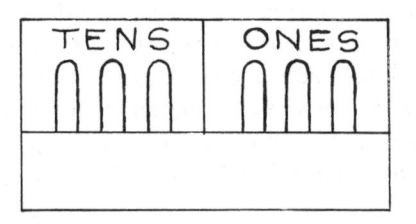

FIGURE 4–7. *Before decomposition*

It is not possible to subtract 8 ones from the 3 ones so it is necessary to decompose the 33 as in Figure 4–8.

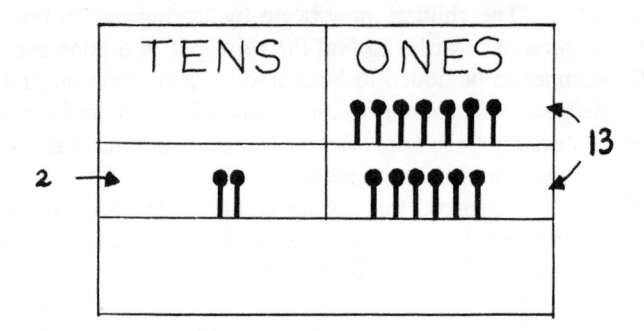

FIGURE 4–8. *After decomposition*

Now subtract 8 ones from the 13 ones and 1 ten from the 2 tens.

Equal Additions Method

The equal additions method of compound subtraction employs the inclusion of a constant. In order for children to use this method with understanding, they need to be familiar with the use of a constant in mathematics. Of course, it is possible for children to learn the equal addition methods, or any other one for that matter, on a purely manipulative level. But if they are to subtract numbers in a meaningful manner, they have to understand the mathematical principles that underlie each basic process. The term "borrowing" has been erroneously associated with the equal additions method of subtraction. Actually, there is no borrowing in the literal meaning of the term involved in this method of subtraction.

As we have said, if students are to utilize the equal additions method of compound subtraction with understanding, as a prerequisite they must have had some experience with the use of a constant. For some primary-level children the operation of a constant may need to be hinted at by the teacher in such a fashion that the "discovery" element is closely structured. For example, the teacher might ask the children, "If the same number is added to both parts of a subtraction problem, is the remainder changed? If the same quantity is added to two addends, is the sum affected in any way?"

There are primary-level children who, with only subtle suggestions from the teacher, can experiment independently with concrete materials to find answers to the two questions above. Others will need to work on the problem with more direct teacher assistance and encouragement. The children may begin by "trying out" a few representative algorisms in order to find the principle of a constant. Using 2 as the number to be added to both sides of a subtraction and addition algorism, the teacher asks the teacher-directed math group to suggest a subtraction algorism with which to work. One child suggests $9 - 2 = 7$. The others agree to use it.

The teacher suggests that for an addition algorism they use the additive inverse of it: $7 + 2 = 9$. Now they are ready to try out adding 2 to each element (number) of the algorism.

$$
\begin{array}{rclcr}
9 & + & 2 & = & 11 \\
-2 & + & 2 & = & -4 \\
\hline
7 & & & & 7
\end{array}
$$

The children, using counters, add 2 as the constant; the resulting algorism is $11 - 4 = 7$. The remainder is not changed by adding the constant. They try many more examples using other constants. In every instance the remainder is not affected. Then the children try using 2 as a constant in an addition algorism.

$$
\begin{array}{rclcr}
2 & + & 2 & = & 4 \\
+7 & + & 2 & = & +9 \\
\hline
9 & & & & 13
\end{array}
$$

Written in another form, the use of the constant looks like this: $(2 + 2) + (7 + 2) = 13$.

Adding a constant to both addends of an addition algorism, the children conclude that the sum *is* affected to the extent of two times the constant. Then the teacher interjects another problem, which sets the children buzzing and anxious to experiment. Perhaps subtracting a constant from each addend would not affect the sum? Better yet, subtracting a constant from one addend and adding it to another addend would not affect the sum. And so goes the experimentation and discovery. As a result, the children can understand that *adding a constant to both numbers of a subtraction algorism does not affect the remainder*. This is the mathematical principle that undergirds the equal additions method of subtraction.

If the reader will check the equal additions approach to the algorism $33 - 18$ shown earlier, he will be better able to follow this explanation. The child is taught to say 13 ones take away 8 ones and 3 tens take away 2 tens.

Why use ten as a constant? We do this because ten is easiest to inject into our decimal system. It is advisable to have children experiment with some constant other than ten after they understand the operation of the constant in the compound subtraction algorism. After experimenting with other constants, the children readily conclude that ten can be employed with the greatest efficiency.

Decomposition or Equal Additions Method?

Does educational research give us any guidelines as to which of the two methods (decomposition or equal additions) will enable children to subtract with greater efficiency? The most significant study in this area seems to be that of Brownell and Moser,[1] which indicates that the decomposition method is most effective if students are to understand the *meaning* of compound subtraction. But if students are to be taught to subtract mechanically, the equal additives method is appropriate, all other factors in the teaching setting being equal. In the final analysis, the effectiveness of either method is dependent upon the effectiveness of the teacher.

Furthermore, with many children it isn't a question of teaching them either one or the other method of subtracting but rather of helping them to understand *several* ways of thinking about one subtraction algorism. To understand *one* method of compound subtraction may be a big enough learning task for some children. But if a child can mentally handle more than one method of attacking compound subtraction, he should be encouraged to explore several methods *and* the meaning behind each one.

Teachers have grossly underestimated children's abilities to deal intellectually with *many* methods of solving a mathematical situation. This in itself is a denial of the opportunity to think flexibly (or creatively).

Zero—A Trap in Subtraction

Zeros in subtraction algorisms can trap and frustrate young subtracters. A great many of the mistakes that children make in handling zeros in subtraction algorisms result from a lack of understanding of the function of zero. (For example, in the number 104 the zero holds the tens place and represents no frequency of that place.) Other student errors result from incorrect regrouping (decomposing) in com-

[1] W. A. Brownell and H. E. Moser, *Meaningful vs. Mechanical Learning: Study in Grade III Subtraction* (Durham, N.C.: Duke University Press, 1949).

pound subtraction algorisms. An example such as the one below can be particularly difficult for many children to handle.

$$302$$
$$- 113$$

Employing concrete materials, particularly place-value devices, can help learners to understand the regrouping necessary to arrive at an accurate answer.

Check and Double Check!

If presented meaningfully, the traditional subtraction check can be valuable to students in demonstrating that subtraction and addition are opposite processes. The children should see subtraction as follows: a number and one of its parts are given; we subtract to find the other part. Therefore, by adding the two parts, the sum should be the original number. The check for subtraction is then depicted in a manner similar to this:

Subtraction	*Addition*
27 sum	9 addend
− 9 addend	+ 18 addend
18 addend	27 sum

Other Methods of Checking Subtraction

There are many other methods of checking subtraction algorisms in addition to the traditional one shown above. The teacher of mathematics may desire to introduce students to some of them or, better still, help children to brainstorm methods of their own. It may be desirable to make suggestions such as the following to students who seem to have difficulty with experimentation: Perhaps it is possible to subtract beginning from left to right. Perhaps it's even possible to begin subtracting in the *middle*. Like in the example 462 − 131, can we begin subtracting with the three tens in 131?

After the children have experimented and tested various techniques and arrived at their own conclusions, the teacher may want to explain that at one time in history people subtracted from left to right. They would scratch out a wrong numeral and change it as needed. This method of subtraction is called the scratch method.

Boxes A, B, and C in Figure 4–9 depict the step-by-step technique of subtracting this way.

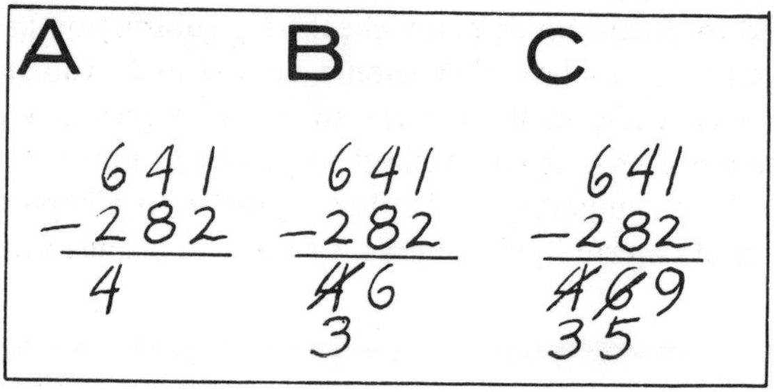

FIGURE 4–9. *Subtracting by the scratch method*

Subtraction can be checked by projecting the algorism into a different base or mod system. For example, Figure 4–10(a) shows

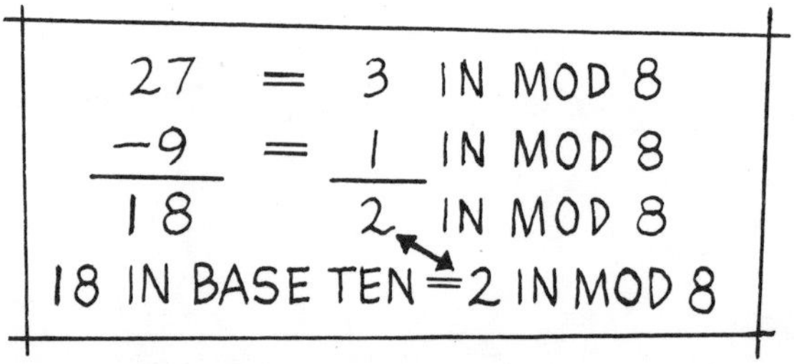

FIGURE 4–10(a). *Checking in mod 8*

the algorism $27 - 9 = 18$ checked in mod 8. (The reader who is unfamiliar with modulus number systems may refer to Chapter 8.)

Figure 4–10(b) shows the same algorism checked in base 5.

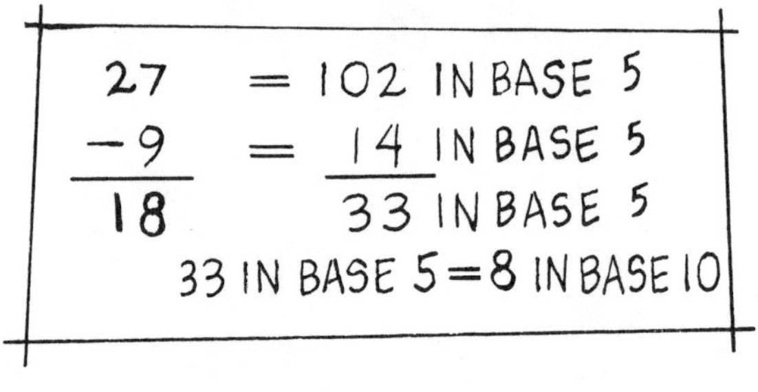

FIGURE 4–10(b). *Checking in base 5*

Subtraction algorisms also can be checked with a different notation, such as ancient Egyptian. Or the check could be made with some concrete number device, such as an abacus. Students should be encouraged to dream up as many checks for subtraction as they can. Then, together, as a class, they should discuss and evaluate the suggestions for checking methods *after* all of the suggestions have been listed. The word *after* is emphasized to point out that deferred judgment may be an important point here. (Refer to Chapter 7 for an explanation of deferred judgment as it relates to brainstorming.)

Creative Multiplication

> . . . *The mathematical facts worthy of being studied are those which, by their analogy with other facts, are capable of leading us to the knowledge of a mathematical law just as experimental facts lead us to the knowledge of a physical law. They are those which reveal to us unsuspected kinship between other facts, long known, but wrongly believed to be strangers to one another.*

> HENRI POINCARÉ, "Mathematical Creation"

Multiplication as Putting Together

"Do you know which newspaper has a name which means the same as multiplication?" a somewhat squeaky voice questioned.

"Ah, I've heard that one. The answer is the *New York Times,*" the second child replied.

Children perceive and come to grips with the multiplication action in a multitude of fashions, not the least of them through the application of their sense of humor. The creative teacher of mathematics encourages and enjoys the levity along with his students and adds his own to it.

"What kind of table doesn't have legs?" a little girl with braids asks her teacher.

"I don't know," responds the teacher, deliberately playing along with a very old riddle.

"Multiplication table," the wee one blurts out excitedly.

Multiplication, in order to be understood by children, must be presented to them using various aspects of the tri-point progression as explained in Chapter 2. In essence, multiplication is a special kind of putting-together action (process) and consequently is a modified form of addition. Multiplication is the inverse of the divisional process much the same as addition is the inverse of subtraction. One generally accepted definition of multiplication is *putting together of two or more groups equal in size without counting.*

* Five in ancient Sumerian.

The commutative and associative laws apply to both addition and multiplication. Why aren't these two laws applicable to subtraction and division? The elements of the multiplication algorism are called *factors*. The solution to the multiplication algorism is frequently referred to as the *product*.

Begin with Basic Combinations

Usually the initial teaching task relative to presenting multiplication to children is the introduction of the basic multiplication combinations. Congruent to addition, there are *one hundred* basic multiplication combinations. The zero combinations (0×1, 1×0, 0×2, 2×0, etc.) traditionally are not presented to children in the *initial* teaching of multiplication. It is difficult to demonstrate socially or with concrete counting materials the zero combinations. Therefore, *excluding* the zero combinations (19), 81 basic combinations remain for initial presentation.

Since division is the inverse of multiplication, many math programs introduce basic multiplication and division at the same time. In multiplication we may multiply one factor times another factor and arrive at a product: $4 \times 5 = 20$ or $5 \times 4 = 20$. Division implies subtracting one factor (4) from the product (20) as many times as possible until zero or a number smaller than the original factor is ascertained: $20 \div 4 = 5$; $20 \div 5 = 4$. Division, then, in simple language, involves dividing a product by one of its factors in order to determine the complementary factor. Thus if division and multiplication are presented simultaneously, children learn (with the exception of the zero combinations) *four basic combinations for each set of two factors*. For example, factors 6 and 3 yield $6 \times 3 = 18$; $3 \times 6 = 18$; $18 \div 3 = 6$; $18 \div 6 = 3$.

The law of commutation shows that the combinations above ($6 \times 3 = 18$; $3 \times 6 = 18$) are mathematically identical; but socially the groupings implied are quite different. For example, 3 groups of 6 Sky Raider Jet Planes is not the same situation as 6 groups of 3 Sky Raider Jet Planes. In both instances there are 18 jet planes involved, but 3 groups of 6 does not appear the same as 6 groups of 3.

Students can easily demonstrate the two distinct groupings by using concrete counters or some other manipulative material. Employing a dot board or a piece of peg board, students can circle different groups of dots or holes with chalk or charcoal as shown in Figure 5–1. The dot board is constructed by painting dots with a waterproof paint on a small piece of ¼-inch plywood, wallboard, pressboard, posterboard, showcard or cardboard. A piece of dark chalk or charcoal is used to circle groups of holes or dots. The chalk or charcoal can be erased with a damp cloth or sponge and the board used over and over again.

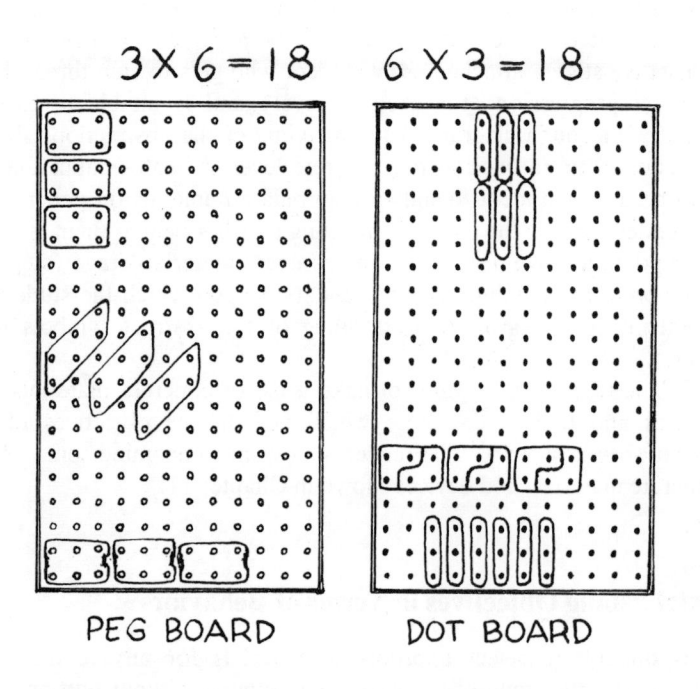

FIGURE 5–1. *Law of commutation illustrated*

Each board shown above depicts 3 × 6 and 6 × 3: 3 groups of 6 and 6 groups of 3. Students may come to recognize that there are a *total* of 18 holes or dots in each set of groupings but that the groupings are different.

The derivation of the word *commutation* is "commute." Many students may know that to commute means to travel back and forth. This associated meaning may help them to recall the nature of the mathematical law connected with the word *commutation*.

Brainstorming Materials for Use in Teaching Multiplication

The teacher certainly will want to interject her own creative thinking in brainstorming various types of concrete materials and devices which will assist her in teaching multiplication. The intellectually less able students will need to utilize more concrete materials for a longer period of time than will most of their peers. This is to be expected, and, if treated in a direct manner, will be accepted by them without a negative stigma attached. *Any* student who gets to step three of the tri-point progression (the abstract level) and is unable to explain and draw a rough diagram of the *meaning* of the abstractions should be required to go back to the concrete level. A mathematics teacher who permits a student to simply manipulate numerals on paper without understanding the concrete meaning that lies behind them is doing the student a grave disservice. The concrete materials stage (step one of tri-point progression) is the foundation upon which the student of mathematics builds his understanding of the abstract symbols used later.

The teacher may want to make a list of concrete materials and devices and then select those which best fit the objectives of his lesson or unit of work. The reader may want to examine some of the concrete materials and devices shown in Chapter 11.

Establishing Objectives in Terms of Behaviors

It is difficult to select appropriate materials for any mathematics lesson—whether multiplication or some other—without putting one's objectives into behavioristic terms. Of course, these objectives, when written as behaviors, must be observable and measurable, or the mathematics lesson cannot be clinically evaluated. Remember, however, that even highly creative mathematics teachers have their objectives firmly and clearly in mind *before* they attempt to select appropriate teaching materials and activities.

Objectives for Mathematics Lessons in Multiplication

The authors have stressed the importance of writing objectives for mathematics lessons in behavioral terms. But what does this mean?

Perhaps an effective method of illustrating behavioristic objectives is to present some samples of objectives for multiplication lessons which are vague and ambiguous and some that are written in terms of child behaviors. Following are a few objectives excerpted from different lesson plans of several student teachers:

Set I

1. Help children to grow in their appreciation of mathematics as a system of related ideas.
2. Help students to understand multiplication.
3. Each child should know basic multiplication combinations at the end of the lesson.
4. Give students experience in using the multiplication process in word problems.
5. Show the boys and girls what the law of commutation is all about.

Set II

(Objectives written in behavioristic terms)

At the close of this lesson most children in the class should be able to:

1. Explain verbally with accuracy that 4×3 and 3×4 represent different grouping patterns but the same product.
2. Demonstrate with concrete counters on their desks the grouping patterns and thereby the products of all basic multiplication combinations using 6 as the multiplier.
3. Illustrate on a pocket abacus the partial products of the following multiplication algorisms:

$$\begin{array}{ccc} 11 & 25 & 19 \\ \times\,6 & \times\,10 & \times\,4 \end{array}$$

4. Explain verbally and accurately that the second partial product in the following multiplication example is set to the left one place because multiplying by a digit in the tens place will always yield a product that is at least the size of ten (unless one of the factors is zero).

$$\begin{array}{r} 27 \\ \times\,15 \\ \hline 135 \\ 27 \\ \hline 405 \end{array}$$

Discuss the differences in the wording of the two sets of objectives. Remember that the objectives listed are not from the same mathematics lesson but were taken from a random sampling of lesson plans written by student teachers.

As an example of the need for stating objectives in terms of children's behaviors, study the first objective listed in Set I. Would you agree that it is a valid one? If it is, how would the teacher know if a child was "growing in his appreciation of mathematics as a system of related ideas"? What *behaviors* would a child evidence if he has achieved the objective?

The Greater Objectives of Mathematics

The authors stress the need to identify behavioristic objectives for mathematics lessons which can be observed and measured during and at the close of one lesson. There are, however, long-range objectives that cannot be accomplished in one lesson, such as developing in children a long-lasting, positive attitude toward mathematics. The authors suggest that any general long-range objective can be broken down into a series of developmental behaviors, any of which can be the target for a single math lesson.

How does a child who is developing a positive attitude toward mathematics behave? The crux of effective lesson planning lies in the clarity, preciseness, and validity of the objectives for the lesson. If the objectives are stated in specific behavioristic terms, planning the appropriate activities, materials, and evaluation for the lesson fall into place logically. The objectives form the frame of reference against which all other aspects of the mathematics lesson should be evaluated. Graphic and dramatic evidence of the vital relationships that exist between the objectives and the accompanying components of a lesson have been demonstrated by Dr. John Readling and Mr. Vincent Barone in the Schenectady-Oswego Project (Schenectady Public School System, Schenectady, N.Y., and State University College at Oswego, N.Y.), 1964–66. Their work is giving new dimensions to what might be called a clinical analysis of the teaching act.

A Close Look at Multiplication

We have already established the fact that concrete learning materials are vital in interpreting a multiplication algorism to children in a meaningful way. A second important point in promoting understanding is identifying the *function* of each *factor* of the algorism. The functions of the factor are usually identified by the terms "multiplier" and "multiplicand." For instance, in 7 × 9, the 7 is the multiplier and the 9 the multiplicand. But these terms can be meaningless to children unless they understand that each term implies a role or function. The multiplier designates the number of equal groups to be added. The multiplicand indicates the size of the groups—in this case, 9. Therefore, 7 × 9 means 7 groups of 9 or 9 taken 7 times. Yet, as a general classification, both 7 and 9 are called "factors" of 63 (the product). Interpreted in grouping terms, 7 × 9 represents 7 groups of 9. Obviously, an alternate manner of expressing this algorism would be 9 added 7 times.

A number line can be very helpful in pointing out the addition of equal groups as the crux of multiplication. On the number line shown in Figure 5–2, 3 × 4 and 4 × 3 are bracketed.

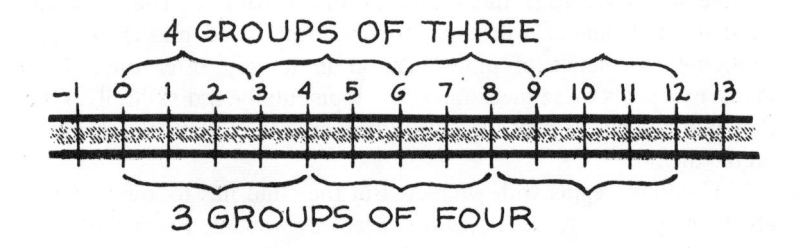

FIGURE 5–2. *Number line with brackets*

Using the same number line and brackets, division can be illustrated as the inverse of multiplication. The top set of brackets indicates 3 ⟌ 12 . How many groups of 3 can be subtracted from 12? Begin at 12 on the number line and count *backwards* by 3. The result is that 4 groups of 3 can be subtracted from 12. Now identify the basic division combination that is illustrated by the lower set of brackets.

A Galaxy of Multiplication Skills

It is not in keeping with the authors' objectives to give a detailed explanation of *all* major phases of the multiplication action. Rather, the authors refer the reader to any of the mathematics methods books listed in the bibliography; all of them explain the basic mechanics of the multiplication process.

The authors strongly recommend that the reader investigate these topics relative to multiplication:

1. Presentation of the basic multiplication combinations.
2. The distributive and associative laws as they apply to multiplication.
3. Zeros in multiplication.
4. The identity element of multiplication.
5. Habituation of the basic combinations of multiplication.
6. Multiplication by a two-digit multiplier.
7. Multiplication by a three-digit multiplier.
8. Checking multiplication.

In the remaining space the authors elect to present some of the more unusual aspects of multiplication—variations on the theme. Helping children to understand that multiplication is plastic and flexible will encourage them to experiment with it. The very able child in mathematics will come to understand and master the conventional mechanics of multiplication in a very brief time if the teacher presents these mechanics developmentally and skillfully. Once they understand the process, *all* children are ready to create variations on the theme.

Creation begins with wonder. But the child has to know enough about the process to develop some areas of wonder. From the standpoint of promoting creative thinking, the only reason for exposing children to what has already been worked out by others (the conventional methods of multiplying), is the provision of a springboard for making modifications. But what causes wonder in the mind of a child? It is the discovery that there is open-endedness regarding some activity to which the child has intense commitment. Open-endedness here means that some aspect of the activity is lacking, is incomplete, that something remains to be accomplished.

Children can recognize multiplication as a fundamental putting-together action that can be interpreted through a host of mathematical notations and settings. Is it possible to multiply using Roman numerals? After checking the efficiency of Roman numerals as employed in multiplication, students may be challenged to try projecting the multiplication process into other ancient systems of notation. Using either or both of the ancient systems shown in Chapter 3, experiment to determine if multiplication can be executed in those systems.

Fostering Flexible Thinking by Varying the Notation

For a seemingly rigid algorism like 6 times 296, an amazing variety of notations can be developed. One variation is to use extended notation: $p = (6 \times 200) + (6 \times 90) + (6 \times 6)$. Two other variations are: $p = 6 (148 + 148)$ or $296 + 296 + 296 + 3 (296)$.

Another variation is to multiply the partial products in reverse order:

$$
\begin{array}{r}
296 \\
\times\, 6 \\
\hline
1200 \\
540 \\
36 \\
\hline
\end{array}
$$

Supply some variations of your own.

Constructing a set of Napier's bones and using them to multiply is another activity that can add variety and interest to the presentation of multiplication. Napier's bones are described later in this chapter.

Multiplication with Binary Numeration

The multiplication action can easily be projected into a numeration system that utilizes a base other than 10. In fact, providing an opportunity for children to do this can be a good test of whether or not they really understand multiplication. One numeration system other than the familiar decimal system (base 10) that can be employed is the binary system (base 2). *All* of the basic multiplication combinations in binary are 1×0; 0×1; 1×1 and 0×0. Once a learner has these combinations mastered he has *all* of the combinations needed to execute *any* multiplication algorism in base 2 (binary).

In the event the reader is unfamiliar with the mechanics of a binary numeration system, see Chapter 11. Some students may elect to project multiplication into another base system, such as a quinary system (base 5) or duodecimal (base 12).

The multiplication action can be concretely illustrated by a modulus number system. See Chapter 8 to reinforce your understanding of such a system.

Multiplication and the Ancient Egyptians

The ancient Egyptians developed a mathematical notation system that was functional; a chart of it was shown in Chapter 3. However, although functional in terms of recording quantitative ideas, this system was cumbersome for computation. So the Egyptians devised various devices and techniques for avoiding many of the difficulties of mathematical computation. Among their ingenious schemes was a method of avoiding the complexities of multiplication which has come to be known as *duplation*. The word "duplation" is derived from "doubling," which is the basis of their method. Duplation forced the Egyptians to do more work in multiplication, but the nature of the computation involved is less complex than that in the method of multiplication most familiar to us. Duplation (or doubling), which is still used in some parts of the world in modified forms, encompasses two steps:

1. Make a table of the multiplicand by doubling it several times.
2. Select from the table the products that are called for by the multiplier.

These two steps may sound complicated, but in actual practice they are not. Let us compute the multiplication algorism 27×53 using the duplation method. Figure 5–3 indicates how this can be easily accomplished. The product of 2×53 is derived by doubling the product of 1×53; the product of 4×53, by doubling the product of 2×53. Mentally fill in the blanks shown in the box. This satisfies step one of the duplation method.

$$
\begin{array}{rcl}
1 & \times\ 53\ = & 53 \\
2 & \times\ 53\ = & 106 \\
4 & \times\ 53\ = & 212 \\
8 & \times\ 53\ = & 424 \\
16 & \times\ 53\ = & 848 \\
? & \times\ 53\ = & ? \\
? & \times\ 53\ = & ?
\end{array}
$$

FIGURE 5–3. *Step one of the duplation method*

Step two involves selecting the products that are called for by the multiplier. The reader should recall that the algorism we are solving is 27×53. This literally means 53 added 27 times or 27

53's. Look at Figure 5–4. Locate the product of 32 × 53 in the box. Thirty-two times 53 is too much; we only need to compute 27 times 53. From the box we can use 16 × 53, which equals 848. Now if we add to this product the product of 8 × 53 we would then have 24 times 53. Then to finish out the computation we add 106 and 53.

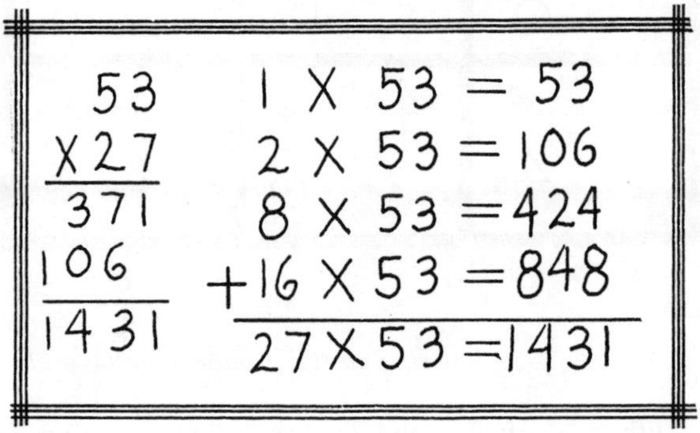

$$53$$
$$\times 27$$
$$371$$
$$106$$
$$1431$$

$$1 \times 53 = 53$$
$$2 \times 53 = 106$$
$$8 \times 53 = 424$$
$$+16 \times 53 = 848$$
$$27 \times 53 = 1431$$

FIGURE 5–4. *Step two of the duplation method*

Lattice or Grating Method of Multiplication

Another ancient method of multiplication involves writing the partial products on a grid. This method has been assigned several names, among them lattice, grating, and jalousia.

To multiply 26 × 483, for example, the grid is constructed with three squares horizontally (because the multiplicand contains three digits) and two squares vertically (because the multiplier contains two digits). Study Figure 5–5 to determine the manner in which the partial products are entered on the grid.

After all of the multiplication has been completed, the final step is to add the partial products *diagonally*.

Children could be taught to use this lattice method of multiplication simply as a manipulative trick. But as such it has little meaning or value in terms of helping them to understand mathematics. The question that should accompany the presentation of the lattice method is: Why does it work? How is this grid method related to Napier's bones (discussed later in this chapter)?

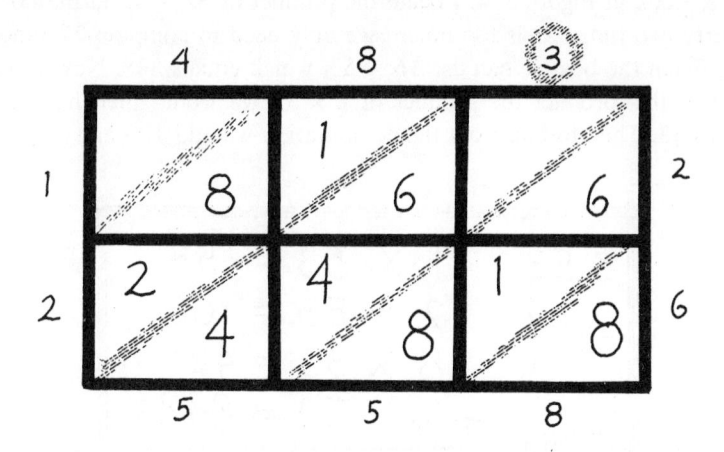

FIGURE 5–5. *Entering partial products on the grid*

The authors do not intend to imply that exposing children to the lattice method of multiplication will prompt them to engage in creative thinking. Lattice multiplication, however, coupled with many other methods of multiplication, can foster the understanding that multiplication can be approached in a vast number of ways. Once the children realize that the door to innovation stands open, they may burst forth and strike out on a pathway they alone can see. Perhaps the most important function of the teacher is to assist in identifying open doors.

Hunting for Short Cuts

In terms of the mental processes involved, hunting for more efficient methods of solving an algorism is a form of creative thinking. In order to come up with a mathematical short cut the learner must toy with *several* methods of solving the algorism. He must, of necessity, examine and reject less efficient solutions to the algorism. Thus the hunting process can become a creative exercise.

Somerset Maugham expressed it this way: "Imagination grows by exercise. Contrary to popular belief, it is more powerful in the mature than in the young." And so, following this thread of reasoning, the mathematics teacher must cajole, challenge, plead with, and encourage his students to begin the "hunt" for variations. During this process students will naturally go through the four intellectual steps that have been identified by psychologists as components of creative thinking: preparation, incubation, illumination, and verification.

* * *

Miss Ellis is constantly teasing her mathematics students with the phrase, "Oh, come on now, there must be a better way to do this." It reflects an attitude toward problem-solving that recognizes a need for improvement and constant metamorphosis. In fact, the creative process is frequently defined as *the process of change*—not change for its own sake but change which offers the promise of improvement.

Like Miss Ellis, the teacher, while working with students on the multiplication action (process), can encourage and nurture an approach to problem-solving that constantly asks the question: How else can the same task be accomplished?

In multiplying one two-digit number by another two-digit number, a wide spectrum of short cuts can be devised by children. Miss Ellis decides to expose her students to a few multiplication short cuts as spurs to creative thinking; she hopes that the examples will stimulate other ideas in their minds. Miss Ellis sets up some sample algorisms to help her students discover how to substitute new factors for the old factors to simplify multiplication. The substitution, or renaming of factors as it is sometimes called, represents a short cut in multiplication and its mechanics as follows: $18 \times 45 = 9 \times 2 \times 45 = 9 \times 90 = 810$. Nine and 2 are substituted for 18.

By multiplying 2×45 we get as product a round number (90) that can easily be multiplied by 9.

Another example of multiplication by a two-digit number substituting factor is: $35 \times 14 = 35 \times 2 \times 7 = 70 \times 7 = 490$.

Mentally find the products for the multiplication algorisms that follow: $24 \times 25 = $ ____; $16 \times 15 = $ ____; $12 \times 45 = $ ____.

The teacher may simply write an algorism such as 11×55 on the greenboard and then permit his class to openly discuss possible short cuts. Such a step often can be stimulus enough to trigger a brainstorming session with some groups of students. One student may suggest that multiplying by 11 is like multiplying by 10 and adding one more frequency of the multiplicand, i.e., $11 \times 55 = 10 \times 55 + 1 \times 55$. This idea may be the springboard for other short cuts. Multiplying a number by 12 is like multiplying by 10, doubling the multiplicand, then adding the total product, i.e., $12 \times 24 = 10 \times 24 + 2 \times 24 = 240 + 48 = 288$.

When 15 is one of the factors of a multiplication algorism the computation can be easily shortened. Fifteen is composed of 10 and 5. The product of 10 times a number is twice the size of the product of 5 times the same number. Therefore, to multiply any number quickly by 15 simply multiply it by 10. Five times the same number is one half of the product of 10 times the number. For example, to multiply 15 times 144 multiply 10 times 144, which yields 1440. One half of 1440 is 720, and this represents 5×144. Now add 720 and 1440. The sum, 2160, represents the product of 15×144.

Two-Digit Multiplication "Like Lightning"

To facilitate speed in multiplication by a two-digit number, as well as to present another variation of the multiplication action, the teacher may demonstrate cross multiplication to his students. Cross multiplication is also called the *lightning method* of multiplication; it is taught extensively to children in European elementary schools. Its major objective is to simplify two-digit multiplication to such an extent that it can be done *mentally*, without paper and pencil. The product is obtained almost instantly—"like lightning." For example, let us try cross multiplication on this algorism: 41×32. It certainly would be difficult for many children to arrive at the final product without using pencil and paper. But with cross multiplication, the final product can be obtained almost instantly. By teaching children to examine the algorism closely it can be pointed out to them that the first numeral of the product will be 2. This can be safely stated because the numeral that appears in the *ones* place of the first partial product is *always* the first numeral in the final product. So the first numeral of the product can *always* be obtained by multiplying the numeral in the multiplier (one factor) that occupies the ones place times the numeral in the multiplicand (second factor) that holds down the ones place. In this case the numerals are 1 and 2 respectively. (See the computation below.) By multiplying the 1 that is circled times the 2 that is

$$
\begin{array}{r}
3\,② \\
\times\ 4\,① \\
\hline
\text{x}\,② \\
\text{XXX}\downarrow \\
\hline
2
\end{array}
$$

circled we know that 2 will be the first numeral in the *final product*. Likewise, by multiplying the 4 in the multiplier by the 3 in the multiplicand, we can determine the numeral or numerals that will appear in the place or places farthest to the left in the final product. (This operation is shown below.) This is assuming nothing is carried over

$$
\begin{array}{r}
32 \\
\times\ 41 \\
\hline
X2 \\
12\quad X\!\downarrow \\
\hline
12\quad X2
\end{array}
$$

from the tens place. And so we can determine rapidly that the final product will be 12 ? 2. The only numeral we have not identified is that in the tens place in the *final* product. This number can be obtained by multiplying the 1 in the multiplier by the 3 in the multiplicand and the 4 in the multiplier by the 2 in the multiplicand. These two multiplications cross each other as shown below. It is from this action that

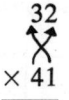

the method derives its name—cross multiplication. The sum of the two products ($1 \times 3 + 4 \times 2$) yields the numeral in the tens place of the final product. One times 3 yields 3 and 4 times 2 yields a product of 8. (Again refer to the box to check this.) The sum of these two products is 11 (in reality 110).

Since two digits cannot appear in the tens place the 1 is carried over into the one hundreds place. This makes the final product 1312.

The explanation of cross multiplication may appear to be complex and cumbersome, yet the process is really simple. With some practice children can master it in a relatively short period of time.

Napier's "Bones"

John Napier, a Scottish mathematician who lived from 1550 until 1617, fathered many unique ideas relative to mathematics. He lived during a period in history when the great masses of Europe, notably the peasant working class, had little if any education as we know it today. Most of them were illiterate and had little or no skill in the four basic mathematical processes. Naturally, they did not know the basic multiplication combinations to which every child is exposed in a modern elementary school.

John Napier set about the task of developing a mathematical aid that anyone could use to determine the products of basic multiplication combinations. He took the table of basic multiplication combinations as shown in Chapter 5 and cut it up vertically into rods. Then he made pocket-sized multiplication rods, which he carried about and proudly demonstrated. The rods became so closely associated with him that they were humorously referred to as Napier's "bones." A set of Napier's bones is shown in Figure 5–6.

The first bone is the "index bone," which contains a vertical listing of factors. The first digit at the top of each bone is another index factor. The index factors are shown in italics on the bones. A set of

FIGURE 5–6. *A set of Napier's "bones" or rods*

"bones" can be constructed easily by students using a variety of materials. Ice cream sticks or tongue blades make handy pocket-sized "bones."

Using the Bones for Computation

For single-digit multiplication (such as 6×7) the bones are employed in the same manner as a multiplication table. To find the product of 6×7 you need only two bones—the index bone and the 6 or 7 bone. If the two bones are placed side by side (as shown in Figure 5–7) the product can be determined by tracing it to the intersection of the 6 and 7, which is circled. The index bone and the 6 bone or the index bone and the 7 bone can be used to find the product of the two factors 6 and 7.

To multiply 43×57, the index bone is used as it is for all computation with Napier's bones. In addition, either the 4 and 3 bones *or* the 5 and 7 bones should be used. When a two-digit number is involved in the multiplication algorism the bones yield only the *partial products,* so it is necessary to do some addition work to arrive at the *total product.*

Will the Use of Napier's Bones Promote Mathematical Creativity in Children?

The *specific* idea of multiplication rods or "bones" does not present an immediate open-ended problem for children. The idea of a multiplication device in the form of rods was the creative product of John Napier. But Napier's bones can serve as a springboard from which children can develop mathematical variations of their own. This question could be posed to the children who have studied the use of Napier's bones: Could some type of rods similar to Napier's be constructed which would serve as computational aids for addition, subtraction, and division? Attempt to devise some.

Can you think of any changes that would improve the bones? Perhaps cards could be used in place of the rods. Can you design another type of device that could be used as an aid in multiplying large numbers?

Number Squabble

To use Number Squabble in the classroom you need this equipment: a group of human beings (preferably mathematics students), some small cards, and an equal number of straight pins. Number Squabble

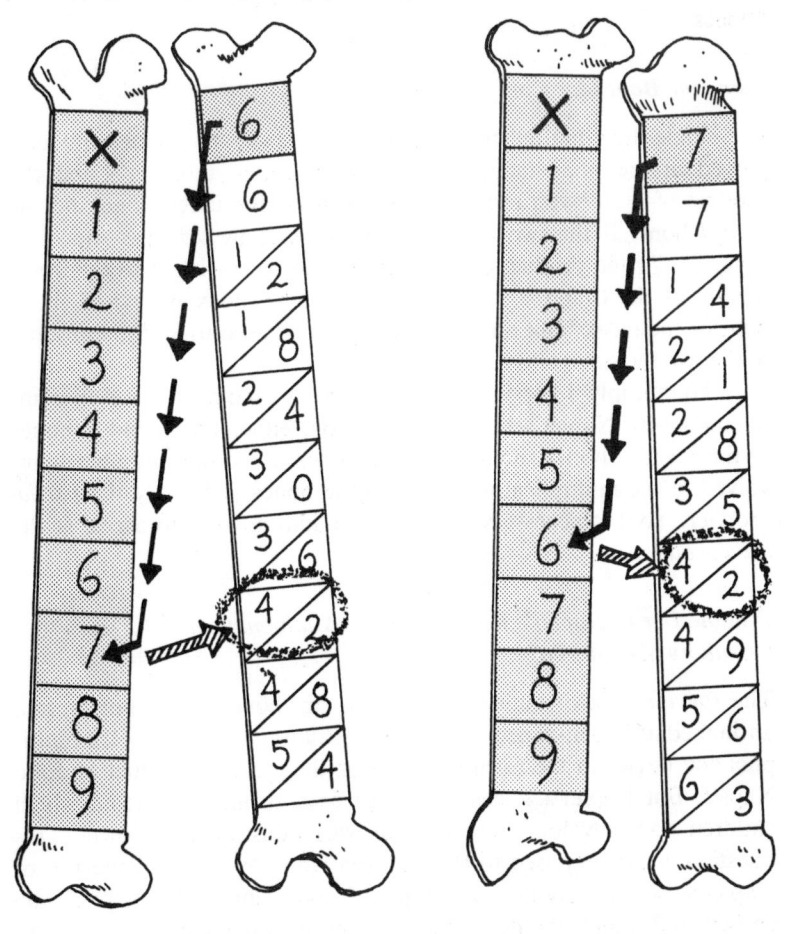

FIGURE 5–7. *Multiplying with Napier's bones*

can be played with any one of the four basic processes (addition, subtraction, multiplication, and division) or combinations of them.

To organize a game of Number Squabble in your classroom, you will first need to select several students to assist you as scorekeepers. If possible, it is best to have four scorekeepers: the teacher and three students. Usually the scorekeepers are positioned around the classroom as shown in Figure 5–8. The children's desks, chairs, and tables will need to be pushed to the sides of the classroom, leaving the floor space clear in the center. Each child is issued a card and a straight

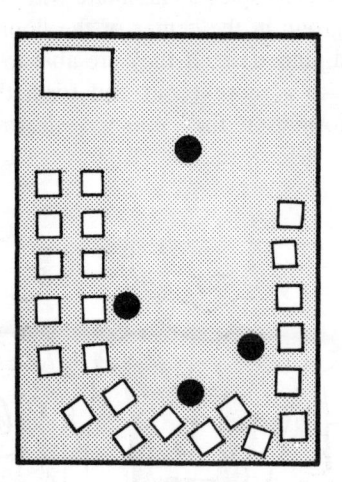

● **= POSITION OF SCOREKEEPERS**

FIGURE 5–8. *Positioning in Number Squabble*

pin, and instructed to pin the card on his clothing. A small numeral appears in the corner of each card and a large numeral in the center, as shown in Figure 5–9. The teacher constructs the cards in advance.

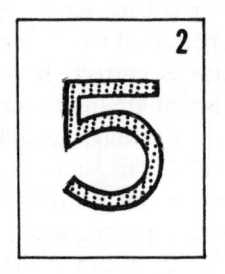

FIGURE 5–9. *Number Squabble card*

Each of the ten symbols 0–9 is written on at least one card. There are several cards with the numeral 1 on them, several with the numeral 2, and duplicate cards of many other numerals. While Number Squabble can be applied to any of the four basic processes it is its application to multiplication that will be described here.

The object of this game is to form multiplication combinations. All of the students assemble in the center of the classroom in one large group. A boy with a 2 card spies a classmate with a 3 card. They mill around in the large group in the center of the floor to locate another student with a 6 card pinned on. If they are able to find one, all three students go together to a scorekeeper and form the combination in front of him. The formation they make is shown in Figure 5–10.

FIGURE 5–10. *Giving the answer in Number Squabble*

The multiplication sign and equal sign are assumed to be between the numerals. Therefore, the students have formed the combination 2 × 3 = 6. The scorekeeper checks to be certain that the combination formed by the students is correct. If so, the scorekeeper adds together the small numerals that are in the corners of the cards. If the reader will look again at the drawing, he will observe that the three *small* numerals are 1, 2, and 4. The sum of these is 7, so *each* of the three students receives 7 points for his role in forming the combination. The scorekeeper, using a pencil, writes a small 7 on the card of each student, after which they return to the large group (the pack) in the center of the classroom. There they try to form *other* multiplication combinations with other students. At the end of a prescribed time limit, such as fifteen minutes, the student that has been able to accumulate the greatest number of points wins the game.

Number Patterns Using Multiplication

Without warning the students in advance that a number pattern is about to be presented, ask them to multiply a couple of combinations for you and record their answers: Boys and girls, please multiply $1 \times 8 + 1$ and record your answer [9]. Now multiply $12 \times 8 + 2$ and record your answer [98].

Fairly soon in the number progression, students will be heard to say things like, "Oh, I see what's happening," and "I know what the next answer is already without figuring it out." The children will find number patterns utilizing multiplication great fun. There is also a challenge to detect a pattern as soon as possible.

$$1 \times 8 + 1 = 9$$
$$12 \times 8 + 2 = 98$$
$$123 \times 8 + 3 = 987$$
$$1234 \times 8 + 4 = 9876$$
$$12345 \times 8 + 5 = 98765$$
$$123456 \times 8 + 6 = 987654$$
etc.

$$11 \times 11 = 121$$
$$111 \times 111 = 12321$$
$$1111 \times 1111 = 1234321$$
$$11111 \times 11111 = 123454321$$
$$111111 \times 111111 = 12345654321$$
etc.

$$12345569 \times \ \ 9 = 111, 111, 111$$
$$12345679 \times 18 = 222, 222, 222$$
$$12345679 \times 27 = 333, 333, 333$$
$$12345679 \times 36 = 444, 444, 444$$
etc.

$$0 \times 9 + 1 = 1$$
$$1 \times 9 + 2 = 11$$
$$12 \times 9 + 3 = 111$$
$$123 \times 9 + 4 = 1111$$
etc.

Simply exposing students to number patterns developed by *others* will not offer them an opportunity to exercise their own creative thinking. Established number patterns can, however, serve to stimulate some students to try developing original number patterns. Not only should students be encouraged to develop original number patterns but, equally as important, they should be challenged to explain why the patterns develop.

Graphing Multiplication on a Rectangular Coordinate System

It is possible to represent various mathematical operations on what mathematicians call the rectangular coordinate system. Children in the middle grades can become proficient at plotting points on graphs of their own making. Study Figure 5–11. The rectangular coordinate system is a method of locating any point on a flat surface or plane. The plane is defined by two intersecting perpendicular lines: X and Y. The horizontal line is called the X axis and the vertical line the Y axis. The intersection of the two axes is called the origin. The position

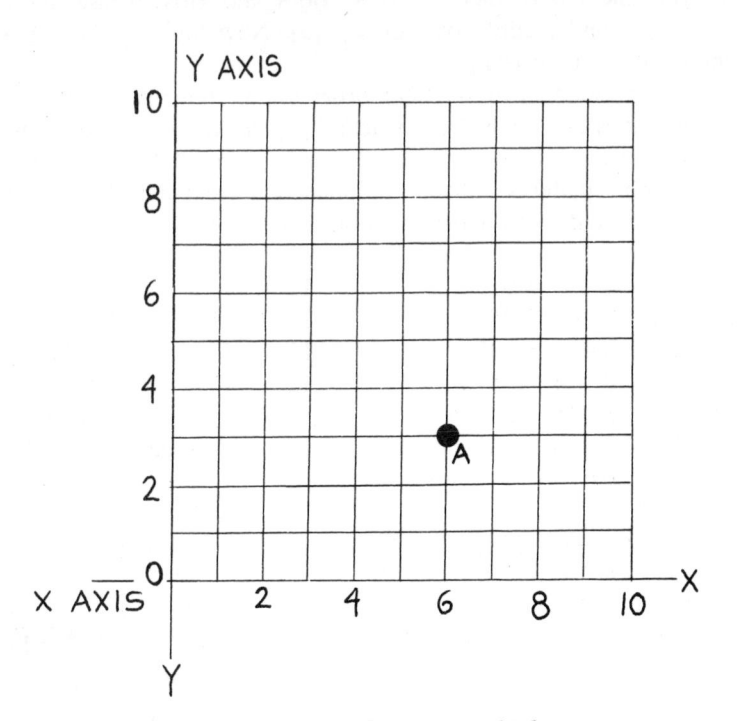

FIGURE 5–11. *The graph used in multiplication*

of any point on the plane can be determined by its relationship to the
X and Y axes. The X and Y values of a point are called the coordinates of the point. The coordinates of a point, when written, are
separated by a comma and enclosed by parentheses. The value of the
X axis is always written first. Point A on the graph is described as
having coordinates (6, 3). How many equal squares are enclosed in
the area outlined by coordinates (6, 3)? Could the area enclosed by
these coordinates represent the product of 6 and 3? Locate the point
on the graph whose coordinates enclose an area of squares equal to
5 × 2. How could negative coordinates be represented on the graph?
Could division of whole numbers (the quotient) be plotted with the
rectangular coordinate system? What variations might be made in the
kind of graph that serves the rectangular coordinate system? Might
there be a diamond-shaped or triangular-shaped coordinate system?
Try to create some other method of graphing points on a plane.

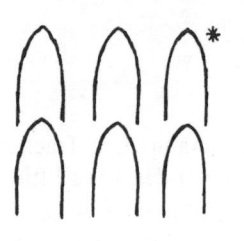 # Fractions in a Creative Mode

Man consists of body, mind, and imagination. His body is faulty, his mind untrustworthy, but his imagination has made him remarkable. . . .

JOHN MASEFIELD, *Shakespeare and Spiritual Life*

Presenting Fractions

"How come when I divide one-half by one-quarter I get two? The answer is bigger than either of the numbers I started with."

"When I multiply two-thirds by one-third the product is two-ninths. Two-ninths is smaller than either of the factors I started with so I guess I really didn't *multiply* anything."

"In dividing a fraction by another fraction, why should I turn the fraction on the right upside down and multiply? I'm supposed to be dividing, not multiplying."

These and countless other questions come from children when they attempt computations with fractions. Presenting fractions to children in a meaningful manner has always been a difficult and challenging task for the teacher. It will always remain so. Space limitations will not permit an extensive presentation here of the multitudinous aspects of this problem. Part of this task should be assumed either by the instructor of your college course in mathematics teaching methods or through in-service workshops. Rather, the authors will deal with some of the major aspects of teaching children fractional ideas that emphasize the promotion of creative thinking.

Fractions are numbers; they belong to the set of *rational* numbers despite the fact that at times they may appear irrational to children. One reason for this is that many fractional ideas and operations are complex and frequently have to be demonstrated and explained to some children in many ways.

* Six in ancient Egyptian.

95

Beware of Superficial Teaching

It is relatively easy to teach children to manipulate fractions as numerals so that they arrive at a correct answer *but* have little or no understanding of the ideas behind the manipulation. For example, a teacher can simply hand to children a manipulative trick that will permit them to multiply fractions successfully: "To multiply a common fraction times a common fraction, multiply numerator times numerator and denominator times denominator." A child can learn to do this in robot-like fashion. He obtains the correct answer, but the manipulation has little if any meaning to him. To avoid this type of superficial teaching the teacher should utilize the tri-point progression, as described in Chapter 2. There should be extensive use of concrete teaching materials that permit the child to actually see and feel fractional divisions and ratios. Most modern mathematics textbooks for the elementary school incorporate a large number of colorful, pictorial representations of fractional ideas. Young children should have some experience dividing objects into fractional parts. The child in the classroom who attempts to cut an apple into *three equal parts* has selected a task around which the skillful teacher can build a host of problems related to fractional ideas that have immediate meaning and importance.

Terminology

The many mathematics textbooks vary as to specific terms that are applied to fractional ideas and operations. However, they do generally agree that a fraction is a numeral. Take, for instance, the fraction $\frac{1}{4}$. Some authors go on to explain that $\frac{1}{4}$ consists of two numerals (1 and 4) or two digits (1 and 4) or two digit symbols (1 and 4). But they all agree that $\frac{1}{4}$ is a numeral representing one basic mathematical idea.

Internal consistency of terminology within a mathematics program is important. Consequently, if the school system in which you teach uses one basic series of mathematics books throughout the elementary school, be sure to use terminology with the children that is consistent with that series.

Before you confront children with mathematics lessons that involve fractions, review mentally the mathematical terminology that you are going to employ. To demonstrate operations with fractions, terms such as these are common: *mixed numeral* (contains a fraction and a numeral naming a whole number, such as 4½); *renaming a fraction* (stating the fraction in different terms).

Other terms you will want to define in your own mind are: *least common denominator, least common multiple, proper and improper fraction, reciprocal of a fraction*, etc.

* * *

Question for discussion: The quest for a *least common denominator* is sometimes referred to as *"seeking a common size part."* What relationship is implied between these two terms?

Fractions Are Continuous, Not Discrete

There are an unlimited number of fractions and the distance between any two fractions can always be subdivided. A fraction is a numeral consisting of one numeral written over another with a fraction bar between them. The denominator can by any digit excepting 0. (Why should zero be excepted as a denominator?) The numerator and denominator define the terms of the fraction.

Meaning of a Fraction

A fraction can convey several specific meanings: an indicated division, part of a whole, or part of a set. What meaning do the numerator and denominator take on in each of the specific meanings given above? When a fraction such as ¾ is used to symbolize the parts of a whole, the 4 indicates the number of *equal parts* into which the whole has been divided. Thus the denominator designates the *size* of the divisional part (¼ would be a larger part of the whole than ⅕). The numerator indicates the number of parts that are being considered. Three fourths indicates the whole as divided into 4 equal parts; 3 of them are being considered. If a child draws the diagram shown in Figure 6–1 to indicate ⅓, what understanding of the meaning of fractions does he lack?

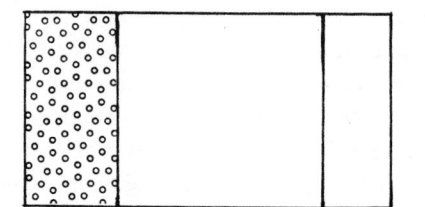

FIGURE 6–1. *Inaccurate conception of one third*

Is ½ Always Equal to ½?

It should be demonstrated to children that any fraction used as a measurement term is theoretically an absolute but in reality an approximation. First, it is impossible to cut an orange *exactly* in half. We do not have measuring instruments accurate enough to divide *anything* exactly in half; there is always a margin of error. Second, a fraction such as ½ is theoretically equal to another ½ only if the same size whole is the unit of reference.

Which Fractions Should We Teach?

Children who understand a particular operation with fractions can successfully inject any fraction into the operation without jeopardizing their understanding of it. But there have been several studies aimed at determining which fractions are used most frequently in business and in daily social living. There is ample evidence that fractions with denominators of 2, 3, 4, 8, 12, 16 and 32 constitute well over 95 percent of all the fractions used in business and social living. Does this fact mean that we, as teachers, should emphasize primarily the fractions that have greatest social utility?

Set Concepts and Fractions

At the present time the term *set* is enjoying wide usage in mathematics nomenclature. The set concept implies classification, a fundamental mental process in which all human beings engage to some extent. Identifying sets and subsets of fractions will strengthen a learner's understanding of fractions. For example, there is the set of fractions whose denominator is a multiple of 2. There is the set of fractions that are equivalent to the whole number 1, i.e., $\frac{2}{2}$, $\frac{9}{9}$, $\frac{15}{15}$, $\frac{64}{64}$, ad infinitum.

Fractions can be employed to express the objects within a set. Figure 6–2 shows a set of dishes. How many dishes are in the set? The fraction $\frac{4}{16}$ indicates what fraction of the set is cups, but it is not in lowest terms. *A fraction is considered to be in lowest terms when the numerator and denominator have no common divisors except 1.*

Set classification of fractions can help children to organize fractional ideas mentally. As a result, the learners may perceive basic operations with fractions as more logical and less difficult. Using set

FIGURE 6–2. *Illustrating fractions*

classification, a fifth grade, with guidance from their teacher, discovered these guidelines:

1. Multiplying the smallest number in a set of numbers by 2, then 3, 4, and so on, will eventually provide the least common multiple of a set.
2. The least common multiple of a set of numbers is the smallest number divisible by all numbers in the set.

The use of open number sentences involving fractions can serve to promote flexible, creative thinking in children. Sentences such as these are open-ended:

$$\tfrac{3}{4} > \square$$
$$\tfrac{5}{6} < \triangle$$
$$\tfrac{1}{2} + \square + \triangle = 3$$
$$\tfrac{1}{8} + \square + \square = 6\tfrac{1}{2}$$

Compose other open-ended number sentences employing the use of fractions.

The Number Line and Fractions

The number line can be an effective teaching aid in demonstrating the relative position of fractions as they relate to whole numbers. Your students can help to create number lines that illustrate different frac-

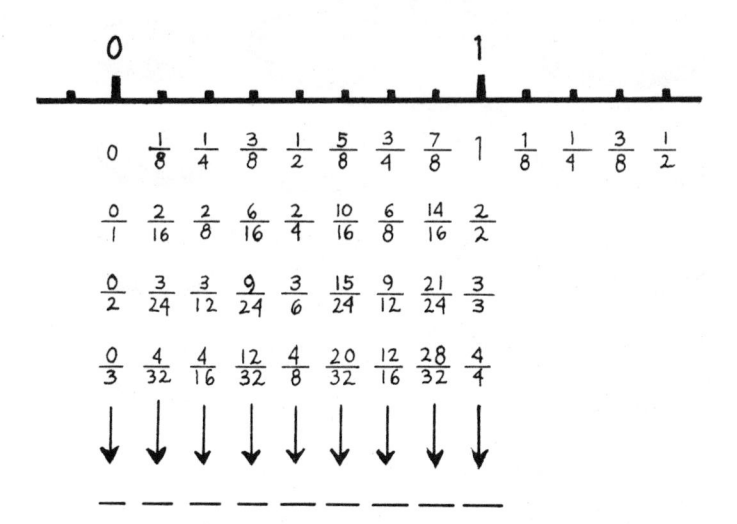

EVERY NUMBER LARGER THAN 0 AND LESS THAN ONE
CORRESPONDS TO A POINT ALONG THE NUMBER
LINE. FILL IN THE BLANKS BENEATH THE
ARROWS. HOW MANY FRACTIONS WOULD LIE
BETWEEN THE ¼ POINT ON THE NUMBER
LINE AND THE ⅜ POINT? IN OTHER WORDS,
HOW MANY FRACTIONS ARE LARGER THAN ¼
BUT LESS THAN ⅜?

FIGURE 6–3. *Fractions along a number line*

tional values. Refer to Chapter 11 of this book for a discussion of
variations and modifications of number lines.

Just as the child illustrates the addition of 15 and 9 by counting
along the number line, so can he add 2½ and ¾ in the same manner.
All four basic operations employing fractions should be portrayed
with a number line as well as with other types of number aids. Construct a number line that will permit you to demonstrate each of the
following operations with fractions:

$$1\tfrac{3}{8} - \tfrac{1}{8} = \square$$
$$2 \ \ - \tfrac{1}{16} = \square$$
$$3\tfrac{1}{4} - 1\tfrac{1}{2} = \square$$
$$6\tfrac{1}{3} - \square \ = \tfrac{3}{23}$$
$$\square + \tfrac{3}{16} = 1\tfrac{1}{2}$$

Creating Your Own Fractional Notation

Once children understand the basic functions of fractions they are ready to create original symbols to represent fractions. Conventional fractional numeration utilizing two digits separated by a line ($\frac{1}{4}$) may not be the most efficient method of recording fractional ideas. There are an infinite number of notational schemes that could be employed to identify the numerator and denominator of a fraction, and more than likely the conventional method can be improved upon. The challenge of "dreaming up" some alternate ways in which fractional ideas could be expressed usually generates a great deal of excitement in the students.

Frequently students will have difficulty "getting started" on this task. Studying about the evolution of fractions will often serve as a springboard from which students can create modifications of their own.

The early Egyptians utilized fractions, first working with unit fractions, later employing a more sophisticated system. The term *unit fractions* implies that the denominator of the fraction remains constant; it is a standard unit. For example, a set of unit fractions could be notated as: $^1\mathrm{x}$, $^2\mathrm{x}$, $^3\mathrm{x}$, $^4\mathrm{x}$, $^5\mathrm{x}$, $^6\mathrm{x}$, etc., where X is a natural number.

The ancient Romans employed unit fractions with 12 and multiples of 12 as denominators. Some historical data indicate that they used a simple system of numeration to record their unit fractions:

$\frown = \frac{1}{12}$	$\approx \ \approx \ = \frac{4}{12}$
$\approx = \frac{2}{12}$	$\approx \ \approx \ \frown = \frac{5}{12}$
$\approx = \frac{3}{12}$	$S \ \ = \frac{6}{12}$

Write the fractions $\frac{1}{12}$ through $\frac{11}{12}$ using Roman symbols as shown above. How could a Roman express the fraction $\frac{2}{3}$ using twelfths?

The ancient Roman system of unit fractions is reflected in their units of measure; for example, *unciae* was $\frac{1}{12}$ of the unit of measurement. Our word *inch*, meaning $\frac{1}{12}$ of a foot, is derived from this source.

The Babylonians employed a system of sexagesimal fractions based upon 60 as the standard unit of partition: $^\mathrm{x}/_{60\mathrm{n}}$ when X and n

are natural numbers. Our system of measuring time in seconds and minutes by divisions of 60 is inherited from the Babylonians.

Our present system of coinage represents a unit fraction system:

$$\text{penny} = \tfrac{1}{100} \text{ of a dollar}$$

$$\text{nickel} = \tfrac{5}{100} \text{ of a dollar}$$

$$\text{dime} = \tfrac{10}{100} \text{ of a dollar}$$

$$\text{quarter} = \tfrac{25}{100} \text{ of a dollar}$$

Encourage children to create an original system of unit fractions including methods of symbolizing the fractions.

Another system of symbolizing fractions has been attributed to the Egyptians. A sampling of them is shown below:

$$\mathsf{C} = \tfrac{1}{2} \quad \mathsf{R} = \tfrac{1}{3} \quad \mathsf{R} = \tfrac{1}{4} \quad \mathsf{P} = \tfrac{1}{10}$$
$$\mathsf{Q} = \tfrac{1}{12} \quad \mathsf{Q} = \tfrac{1}{100} \quad \mathsf{A} = \tfrac{2}{3}$$

Why are many of the symbols shown above particularly appropriate for the fractional ideas they represent?

Combine two or more of the fraction symbols above to equal the fraction $\tfrac{4}{5}$.

The following are a few examples for fraction symbolization created by children in an elementary school:

1. $f = 2 \quad \dfrac{1}{f} = \dfrac{1}{2}; \quad \dfrac{1}{f} 2 = \dfrac{1}{4}; \dfrac{1}{f} 3 = \dfrac{1}{6}; \dfrac{1}{f} + \dfrac{1}{f} 2 = \dfrac{3}{4}$

2. Since fractions imply division, one child suggested this system:

$$3 \,\overline{\smash{\big)}\,2} = \tfrac{2}{3}; \qquad 8 \,\overline{\smash{\big)}\,7} = \tfrac{7}{8}; \qquad 4 \,\overline{\smash{\big)}\,1} = \tfrac{1}{4}$$

3. One child worked out specific colors for the assignment of the values of natural numbers; i.e., red = 2, blue = 3, brown = 4, yellow = 5. This color code was then employed to rotate fractions. Therefore, a red 1 would mean $\tfrac{1}{2}$; a blue 2 would signify $\tfrac{2}{3}$; a yellow 3 would symbolize $\tfrac{3}{5}$, etc.

4. A first-grader suggested drawing a figure to represent "the whole thing" and then darkening in a fraction of it: ▰▱ = $\tfrac{1}{2}$; ▱▰▰ = $\tfrac{2}{3}$. Two and one fourth would be written: 2 ▰▱▱▱

What are some other ways we could write fractions?

Multiplication and Division of Fractions

The authors have chosen to allocate space in this chapter to some of the fundamentals related to multiplication and division of fractions since these are the two operations with fractions which seem to give teachers and students the greatest difficulty. When teaching any mathematical process, it is sound psychology to bring into the explanation previous learnings a child has had, provided they are germane to the process. Children should be helped to discover the patterns (laws) that occur over and over in mathematics and which can be capitalized upon to simplify and understand mathematical operations better. (Remember, however, that there *are* different levels of understanding.)

Using a Property of 1

Multiplying a fraction times 1 or 1 times a fraction appears to be a good initial algorism to use, as it is less complex for children to diagram and operate upon (i.e., $\frac{1}{2} \times 1 = \frac{1}{2}$). One times any number is that number (identity element of 1). The whole number 1 can be renamed as $\frac{2}{2}$, $\frac{3}{3}$, $\frac{4}{4}$, $\frac{5}{5}$, etc. (Is there any closure to this?) Therefore, $\frac{1}{2} \times \frac{2}{2} = \square$ is equal to $\frac{1}{2} \times 1 = \square$; $\frac{4}{5} \times \frac{6}{6} = \square$; $\frac{3}{4} \times \frac{4}{4} = \square$; $\frac{1}{8} \times \frac{5}{5} = \square$.

The foregoing type of operation with fractions leads naturally to this type of algorism: $\frac{2}{3} \times \frac{3}{4}$.

Still using the properties of 1, multiplication of fractions can be demonstrated in this manner:

$$\text{(a)} \quad \frac{3}{4} \times \frac{4}{9} = \square$$

$$\text{(b)} \quad \frac{(3 \times 1) \times (2 \times 2)}{(2 \times 2) \times (3 \times 3)}$$

Is (b) another way of writing (a)? If so, why is it true?

$$\text{(c)} \quad \frac{3}{3} \times \frac{2}{2} \times \frac{2}{2} \times \frac{1}{3} = 1 \times 1 \times 1 \times \frac{1}{3} = \frac{1}{3}$$

Creativity and Diagramming Fractions

A child does not fully understand an operation with fractions unless he can draw a diagram depicting the operation. Much individual creativity can be reflected in the diagrams which pupils construct to illustrate fractional values and operations with fractions. A child, when confronted with the fractional operation below, might illustrate it as shown in Figure 6–4.

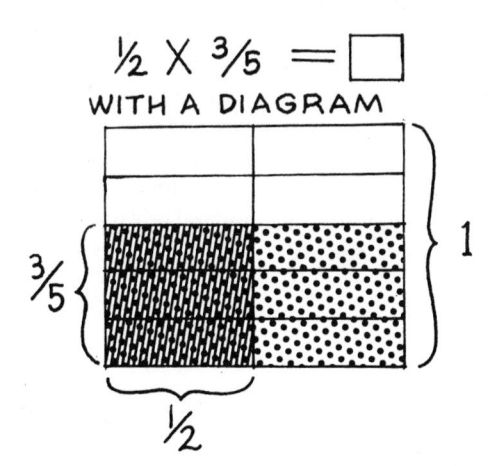

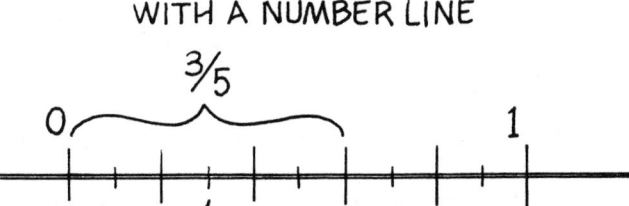

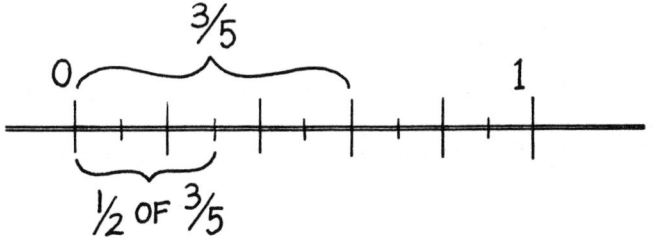

FIGURE 6–4. *Showing fractions in two ways*

There are an infinite number of ways in which any fractional operation can be diagrammed. This is an open-ended aspect of work with fractions where individual creativity can reveal itself. If multiplication involves a series of equal additions, how does the diagram above indicate this fact?

The Key Understanding in Division of Fractions

As already stated, many children are taught to divide fractions by employing a "trick" which the teacher gives them. The trick, of course, is to invert the numerals in the fraction on the right and multiply. For example, $\frac{3}{4} \div \frac{1}{8}$ becomes $\frac{3}{4} \times \frac{8}{1}$. But why does this manipulative trick work?

Before explaining the division operation utilizing fractions, children will need to become familiar with reciprocals. *Reciprocals are two numbers whose product is 1*. Fill in the reciprocal for each empty frame:

$$\frac{3}{5} \times \frac{5}{3} = 1; \; \frac{5}{2} \times \square = 1; \; \frac{1}{12} \times \square = 1; \; 6\frac{1}{4} \times \square = 1.$$

Children need practice and explanation in order to identify reciprocals. Reciprocals are used in division of fractions to simplify the process; they permit us to use one of the properties of 1. After studying the following explanation, identify what property of one is being used.

$$\frac{9}{16} \div \frac{1}{3} = \square$$

This algorism really asks the question: How many $\frac{1}{3}$'s are there in $\frac{9}{16}$? Other ways we could write this algorism are:

$$\frac{1}{3} \overline{\left| \frac{9}{16} \right.} \text{ or } \frac{\frac{9}{16}}{\frac{1}{3}}$$

The form shown above is sometimes referred to as a *complex fraction*.

Now let us assume for a moment that we do not know how many $\frac{1}{3}$'s there are in $\frac{9}{16}$. If we could transform the $\frac{1}{3}$ into a 1 the division would be simplified since any number divided by 1 is _____. (Any exception?) Multiplying $\frac{1}{3}$ by its reciprocal would yield a 1. The reciprocal of $\frac{1}{3}$ is $\frac{3}{1}$. Our algorism now looks like this:

$$\frac{\frac{9}{16}}{\frac{1}{3} \times \frac{3}{1}}$$

The mathematical law of compensation provides that if the divisor is multiplied by a number, the dividend must also be multiplied by the same number. (Why?) Since we are multiplying $1/3$ by $3/1$ we must also multiply $9/16 \times 3/1$. Now our algorism looks like:

$$\frac{\frac{9}{16} \times \frac{3}{1}}{\frac{1}{3} \times \frac{3}{1}}$$

Since we are multiplying $1/3$ by $3/1$, its reciprocal, we know the product is 1. This means our algorism now is:

$$\frac{\frac{9}{16} \times \frac{3}{1}}{1}$$

One divided into any number, except 0, is ______. We can therefore concentrate solely on the fractions above the line ($9/16 \times 3/1$). By simply multiplying these two fractions we will arrive at the quotient for $9/16 \div 1/3$. We begin with $9/16 \div 1/3 = \square$. After using the reciprocal of $1/3$ we ended up with $9/16 \times 3/1 = \square$. So to shorten the process even more, we can assume that the reciprocal has been applied to the fraction that is the divisor ($1/3$) and simply compute the quotient by multiplying $9/16 \times 3/1 = \square$. In other words, we begin with $9/16 \div 1/3 = \square$. Simply by reversing the terms of the fraction on the right and multiplying we have the quotient. You will need to rethink this process several times and apply it to some more division algorisms employing fractions before the operation becomes clear in your mind.

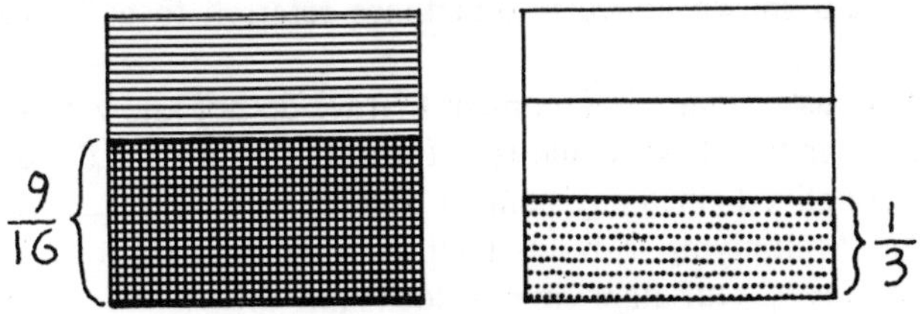

FIGURE 6–5. *Diagramming the algorism*

To begin diagramming the division algorism $9/16 \div 1/3 = \square$ the child might use a ruler and draw the two basic fractional parts shown above. The division example really asks: How many parts the size of the one labeled $1/3$ can be divided into (subtracted from) the part labeled $9/16$? Your eyes will tell you that at least one $1/3$ can be divided into $\frac{9}{16}$ as $\frac{9}{16}$ is $> \frac{1}{3}$. By laying the part labeled $\frac{1}{3}$ on top of the part labeled $\frac{9}{16}$, we can determine what fraction more of the $\frac{1}{3}$ can be divided into (subtracted from) the $\frac{9}{16}$. So now the quotient will be at least 1 plus some fraction of the $\frac{1}{3}$. By carefully measuring the size of the piece left over and comparing it with the size of the $\frac{1}{3}$ being used as the divisor, we find that the remaining piece is $\frac{11}{16}$ *of the one-third used as the divisor.* The quotient is $1\frac{11}{16}$. How can the quotient be $1\frac{11}{16}$ when the two numbers we began with are both smaller ($\frac{9}{16}$ and $\frac{1}{3}$)? The quotient means that there is $1\frac{11}{16}$ one-thirds in nine-sixteenths. To put it another way, we can subtract 1 and $\frac{11}{16}$ *one-thirds* from $\frac{9}{16}$, since division can be conceived of as a series of subtractions. Now try to demonstrate the solution of $\frac{9}{16} \div \frac{1}{3}$ on a number line. It can be done.

Division of fractions is a highly complex operation. Much time and extensive visual teaching aids will be necessary with most children before they understand the meaning behind it. The authors have deliberately used a more complex algorism to demonstrate the operation. With children, the teacher will want to begin division of fractions with a simpler algorism, such as $6 \div \frac{1}{2} = \square$ or $2 \div \frac{1}{3} = \triangle$

Draw a diagram to represent this division example:

$$3\frac{1}{4} \div 1\frac{1}{2} = \square$$

Explain to yourself or to classmates the use of the reciprocal in working this example: $\frac{1}{8} \div \frac{3}{4} = \square$

Try to order the following examples in terms of complexity, beginning with the simplest. Explain your reasoning for the order you have established.

$$\frac{3}{8} \div \frac{1}{2} \; ; \; 2\frac{1}{8} \div \frac{2}{3} \; ; \; 16\frac{4}{5} \div 14\frac{1}{9} \; ; \; 5 \div \frac{1}{4} \; ; \; 2 \div \frac{1}{2} \; ; \; 3 \div \frac{6}{6}$$

Fractions and Different Numeration Systems

Much additional child interest in fractions can be generated by projecting fractions into different numeration systems. As there is no limit (closure) to the number of numeration systems, there is open-endedness for children to project their fractional ideas in this way. For example, let us consider base 12 numeration in relation to fractions. Let the symbol F be the numeral for the number 10 and the symbol ⊏ be the numeral representing the number 11. In base 12 the fraction $\frac{1}{10}$ would read $\frac{1}{F}$ while $\frac{1}{11}$ would appear as $\frac{1}{⊏}$. What fractional value does the numeral $\frac{1}{10}$ have in base 12? Write the numerals to represent these fractional values in base 12: $\frac{10}{12}$, $\frac{6}{15}$, $\frac{1}{24}$, and $\frac{9}{64}$. Now express each of these fractional values in binary numeration.

Create Activities and Devices Employing Fractions

The highly creative teacher is constantly searching for activities and frames of reference into which mathematics can be projected. One such area involves the stock market. A teacher might, for example, give each student a hypothetical sum of money, such as $2,000, with instructions to "buy" common stocks of their choice with it. Since stock quotations are frequently given in fractions of a dollar, the young "buyer" will naturally become involved with them. While $\frac{1}{4}$ of a dollar may not seem to be a significant size fraction, it takes on new meaning if 200 shares of a particular stock advance $\frac{1}{4}$ of a dollar. Every other day or so students can check their $2,000 investments to determine whose investment is earning the most money at that point. Friendly and keen competition often results, but, in the process, students are meaningfully exposed to operations with fractions. This is but one of a limitless number of areas offering practice in this skill.

A fifth-grade student constructed a device to indicate the relative size of fractional parts made from two glass beakers as shown in Figure 6–6. Lines drawn on each beaker enable one to fill the beakers

FIGURE 6–6. *Fractions on beakers*

with colored liquids to indicate fractional parts of the contents of the whole beaker.

Another fifth-grader constructed the device for illustrating unit fractions shown in Figure 6–7. Why do you suppose the builder cut

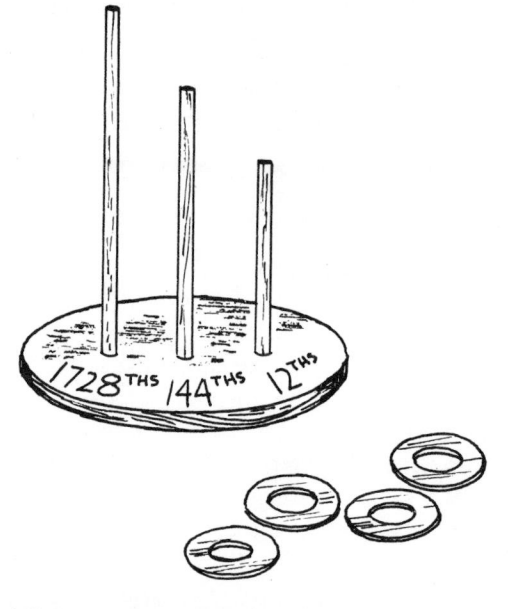

THE METAL WASHERS ARE SLIPPED OVER EACH WOODEN DOWEL TO INDICATE ONE FREQUENCY OF EACH FRACTION.

FIGURE 6–7. *Fractions on dowels*

the dowels to varying lengths? Designing devices to demonstrate fractional values is completely open-ended. Imagination imposes the only limitations.

As with other areas of mathematics, educational games will help to maintain students' interest in fractions and offer practice and reinforcement opportunities. A creative teacher will devise some of her own games as well as incorporating some commercially made ones. There are many commercially produced games dealing with fractions available. One is *The Green Goblin: A Fraction Game,* Whitman Publishing Company, Racine, Wisconsin.

Fractions can be used as the basis for creative writing, original songs and poems, art work, etc. A sixth-grade boy developed this poem about fractions:

> Fractions are the darndest things,
> One-half, one-fourth, one-eighth.
> My father says I need to know them
> To move into the advanced sixth "grath."
> But hard as I try
> I have trouble telling
> A numerator from our auto's carburetor.

* Problem Solving and Creativity

The art of teaching is the art of assisting discovery.

MARK VAN DOREN, quoted
in *Changing Times, The
Kiplinger Magazine*

Injecting Creativity into Problem-solving

One day when a sixth-grade class were working busily at their desks, a student raised his hand to catch the teacher's attention. The teacher strolled over to see if he could be of assistance to the boy. "What's the matter, Jimmy," the teacher asked, "are you having trouble with the math problems?"

Jimmy thought for a few seconds before answering. "Well, yes and no," he confided. "Every time I come up with an answer it just brings up more questions."

Jimmy had put his finger upon a profound mathematical truth. In fact, the scope of Jimmy's comment goes far beyond the field of mathematics. It is typical of a highly creative person to question that which seemingly requires an absolute answer. Creative people are dissatisfied with and suspicious of pat answers to problems. To prove the validity of this position, try to think of a mathematics problem for which there is one absolute answer—an answer that does not need to be qualified. Almost any answer to any problem serves to raise more questions.

The teacher asked Jimmy to share his problem with the entire class, and a lively, probing discussion ensued. Under the stimulus of Jimmy's discerning observation, the class went on to develop some very mature understandings relative to the nature of a mathematical "answer" as well as to the nature of knowledge. What does it mean when a person says he knows "the answer" in mathematics?

Creative problem-solving results from strong personal involve-

* Seven in ancient Mayan.

ment. When students are wrestling with problems in mathematics, they will not stretch their abilities to be creative unless they relate personally to the problem being considered. In the past, mathematics word problems have been lackluster: Johnny has twelve marbles. He gives three of his marbles to his friend Billy. How many marbles does Johnny have left? This type of word problem has haunted mathematics textbooks designed for the elementary school. It is not the type to excite and challenge a child to apply his creative powers in seeking a solution. On the contrary, the marble problem as stated is apt to promote in children the notion that math is a boring, unimaginative collection of naive drivel.

Some current mathematics textbooks for the elementary school show a marked improvement in the nature and character of word problems. But, at best, these problems have to be very general, as the authors of the books are attempting to appeal to the interests of children on a national scale. Here is where the classroom teacher, utilizing his particular knowledge of the interests of his students, can inject some of his own creativity. Using a bit of his imagination, he can alter the word problems that appear in the mathematics textbook to make them of specific interest to his students. Then he can make copies of the problems for all of the class, or a part of it, on a liquid duplicating machine. Students, too, can help to create mathematics word problems for other members of the class.

* * *

Mr. Pagliaro is a fifth-grade teacher in a large city school composed largely of children who come from culturally impoverished homes. Mr. Pagliaro attempts to utilize mathematical word problems that are colloquial and meaningful for his class. For today's mathematics lesson (for group one in his classroom) he has duplicated some problems which he has modified from the standard mathematics textbook.

Mr. Pagliaro begins the lesson by introducing the children to the stick ball design shown in Figure 7–1. He distributes copies of the diagram to the classroom mathematics group. Since most of his students live in crowded tenement areas of the city, they immediately relate in a meaningful manner to the stick ball problems. After all, stick ball is one of their favorite pastimes.

The first problem that Mr. Pagliaro has constructed to accompany the stick ball diagram is this one: If a player hits a home run and runs around all of the bases, how many feet will he run? As the

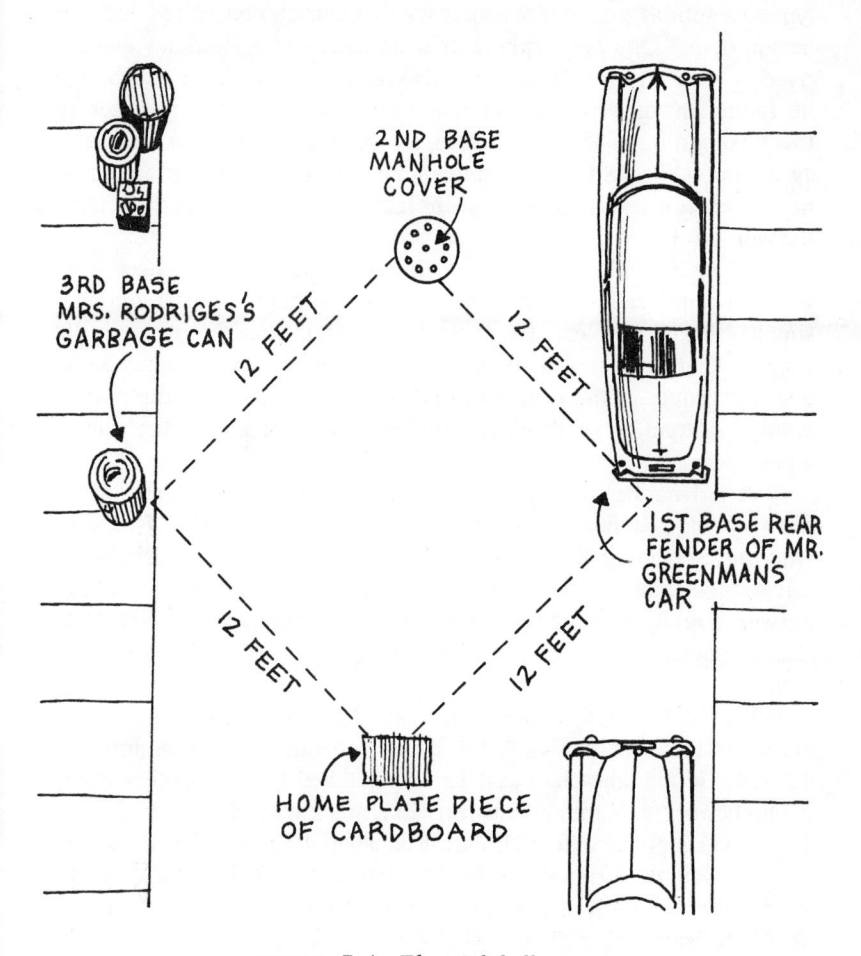

2ND BASE
MANHOLE
COVER

3RD BASE
MRS. RODRIGES'S
GARBAGE CAN

12 FEET

12 FEET

12 FEET

12 FEET

1ST BASE REAR
FENDER OF, MR.
GREENMAN'S
CAR

HOME PLATE PIECE
OF CARDBOARD

FIGURE 7–1. *The stick ball game*

reader can note from the diagram, there are 12 feet between each base. Mr. Pagliaro then turns the mathematics group loose to work out as many "answers" and "ways to find the answer" as they can. One boy serves as a recorder for the group's suggestions.

By the end of twenty-five minutes the group has assembled a list of answers and procedures for finding answers. The group then presents its findings to the entire class. Much lively discussion, thoughtful analysis, and humor accompany the presentation as the class attempts to evaluate the findings of the group. There are many typical solutions plus a few responses that can be considered "off the beaten path." One boy explains that he added 12 four times and arrived at an answer of 48 feet. He also tells the class that even though he found an answer it didn't count, because the runner forgot to touch second base. The class thinks this response humorous; they also agree that while 48 feet is a mathematical solution, the remainder of his answer is not and has no basis in fact, as it cannot be verified from the word problem.

Another child says that he could not arrive at any "answer" that was mathematically accurate because not enough information was supplied in the problem. He goes on to explain that the problem did not say whether or not the person running the bases ran exactly along a straight route. If the runner did not run exactly straight, the answer would be larger or smaller than 48 feet. The class agrees that this is a good point.

A girl in the math group named Sarah reports that she did it the lazy way. "I just wrote the answer like this: 4 (12), and then whoever is reading the answer will have to figure it out for themselves." The class, with Mr. Pagliaro's guidance, decides that Sarah's answer is really another way of recording the original problem using shorter notation and, as such, does not supply an answer to the problem.

Hubert Mitchell, another member of the group, suggests to the class that the answer is 48 feet because you can get it by multiplying 12×4. He tells the class that he has watched his big brother doing his homework in math and has learned a quick way of writing 12×4. It can be simply written 12^4, and it is called 12 to the fourth power. A rather lengthy explanation by Mr. Pagliaro and discussion by the class follows. Finally it is resolved that 12 times itself 4 times is not at all the same operation as 12×4 and the answers to each are vastly different.

And so the various "answers" and "procedures for solution" keep coming from the math group. Before Mr. Pagliaro realizes it, the entire mathematics period has slipped away and only one word problem has been dealt with. Although somewhat frustrated because more of the word problems have not been "covered" in the morning's math period, he knows that some exciting processes have occurred within his students and himself as a result of permitting greater flexibility in the daily math lessons. In summary:

1. Mr. Pagliaro used some of his own creative abilities to modify the original math word problem as it appeared in the textbook. The

4 × 12 mathematical situation was unchanged from the way it had appeared in the book, but Mr. Pagliaro wrote it into a word problem to which *his* particular class would be more apt to respond favorably.

2. He permitted time for the math group to toy with possible "answers" and "procedures" for solving the problem without teacher direction.

3. He provided time for the group to report and explain its findings to the entire class.

The students in Mr. Pagliaro's classroom are developing that flexible, experimental approach to problem-solving which is the keystone to creativity in mathematics. They know from the many answers and procedures that were suggested by their classmates that mathematics is not a system of absolutes.

But, unfortunately, it is unlikely that Mr. Pagliaro's students will continue to develop this flexible approach to problem-solving from exposure to just a few lessons such as the one described. Long-lasting and firmly supported attitudes are developed in children gradually as a result of systematized mathematics experiences. Mr. Pagliaro's students were able to exercise such flexibility in relation to math problem-solving partly because several teachers who taught the students in previous years had promoted it. Miss Pyke helped to do it when she discussed with children the problem: How many ways can the quantity 4 be written? After formulating a huge list of notations, such as $(3 + 1); 2^2; (5 - 1); (1 + 2 + 1); 2\overline{\smash{\big)}8}$; etc., the class decided that there was an indefinite (infinite) number of ways in which the quantity 4 could be notated.

Mrs. Bedeaux, another previous teacher, helped the students recognize that measurement in mathematics was only an approximation. The class developed the generalization that any measurement was only as accurate as the instrument being used to make the measurement. This discussion evolved in Mrs. Bedeaux's fourth grade as a result of a disagreement between two students relative to the *exact* size of an inch.

These and other experiences had contributed to the flexibility with which Mr. Pagliaro's class was able to perceive the problem and formulate methods of attacking it.

Mathematical problem-solving should be the nucleus of any mathematics curriculum that seeks to promote creativity in students and teachers. This is not a revolutionary suggestion; word problems have always been an integral part of mathematics. The difference between a classroom program that promotes creativity and one that inhibits it is the manner (method) in which problem-solving is presented to and used by the students.

In the past teachers were encouraged to give children an organized pattern, called formal analysis or formal logic, for solving math problems. Perhaps this approach to problem-solving was given to you as a part of your mathematics training. There are several versions of formal analysis, but in general it goes something like this: The child is instructed to

1. Read the problem.
2. Find what is given.
3. Find what is asked for.
4. Decide what process to use.
5. Estimate the final answer.
6. Work it (do the computation).
7. Check it.

While formal analysis does offer the user a step-by-step pattern for solving problems, it is also a mental strait jacket. When thinking creatively, an individual does not always follow a logical, step-by-step approach. Many highly creative children will skip entire steps in their thinking and arrive at a more unique solution. The authors recommend that after children have had an opportunity to work on a common mathematical problem, the teacher encourage several children to verbalize their approach or approaches to the problem. When this is done frequently, class members will begin to realize that there are many ways to interpret and attack a given mathematical problem.

Research indicates that errors in problem-solving and decision-making result from omitting some critical stage in the process. One of those most commonly skipped is what the earlier model makers called the "preparation stage." Today this is known as "problem exploration" (seeing just what the mess is) and "problem definition" (what is the *real* problem?). The "idea-getting" stage, also, is often missed, as is the stage where the student should formulate criteria for judging and evaluating ideas or possible solutions. Finally, there is frequently weakness when it comes to elaborating or implementing the solution after it has been found.

Our identification of the four stages of problem-solving represents an immense simplification. The reader might want to investigate a more complex model such as the one suggested by J. P. Guilford in "Intelligence: A 1965 Model," from the *American Psychologist,* 1966, *21,* 20–26. Particularly notable in this model is the constant dynamic process of drawing from one's memory bank and evaluating.

Problem-solving is the stuff of life. Creative students thrive on the challenge of an exciting mathematical problem. What's more, they like to consider many alternatives in solving a problem. The highly creative students usually show a preference for complexity—they enjoy a complicated problem. In dealing with problems in any area, creative students seem to possess the ability to move "between" facts and the mind below the level of consciousness. Many creative students have described their own creative thinking as being "flashes of insight." They do not always adhere to facts but are sensitive to vague feelings and hunches which others would dismiss as ridiculous. These are but a few of the descriptions assigned to the creative problem-solver in mathematics or any other area.

Brainstorming and Mathematical Problem-solving

If children are to be creative in solving mathematical problems they must be encouraged to develop flexible thinking. The classroom teacher actually can teach children to do this. While the teacher may not want to label it as such, the technique of brainstorming can be effectively used with young children as a teaching method. Brainstorming already has proven to be valuable in promoting more fluency and flexibility with ideas when applied to certain types of problem-solving. If the reader is unfamiliar with the techniques of brainstorming he will find the following references useful: Alex F. Osborn's *Applied Imagination,* Charles Scribner's Sons, New York, 1953, Chapter XIII; and Sidney J. Parnes' and Harold F. Harding's *A Source Book for Creative Thinking,* Charles Scribner's Sons, New York, 1962, Part IV.

Brainstorming Teaching Methodology

Brainstorming as demonstrated and described at the University of Buffalo involves *group* interaction. The process is frequently termed "group ideation." But an individual teacher can use the general principle of brainstorming to develop a broader scope of mathematics methodology.

* * *

June Myers, a fourth-grade teacher, realizes that her class of youngsters is weak in solving mathematical word problems. She decides to devote a few weeks to helping her class improve their word-problem skills. But how to present word problems to her class for many days without losing their interest? June decides to brainstorm some ways. She takes paper and pencil and lists all of the methods of presenting problems to children she can think of—no matter how ridiculous they might seem at first thought. This process takes about half an hour. Just as in group brainstorming, June writes down every idea that comes to her mind. She does not permit herself to judge the practicality of the ideas; that can be considered later. Here is a portion of the list that June devised:

1. Word problems without any numbers in them.
2. Silly problems that have many possible answers.
3. Pictures from which students are asked to make up word problems.
4. Word problems that include names of some class members in them.
5. Problems that have missing numbers which can't be solved.
6. Problems that have extra numbers in them.
7. Have children solve problems without using any numbers but by drawing a rough diagram to illustrate the problem and the solution
8. Dramatize (role play) a few math problems employing children in the class.
9. Put algorisms on the blackboard. Have children write problems to fit the algorisms.
10. Take a short walking field trip to cafeteria or boiler room. Construct some math problems related to the field trip.

Applying Brainstorming to the Solution of Word Problems

A teacher can encourage and demonstrate the use of brainstorming with the three phases of a mathematical problem—definition, examination, and interpretation. *Methods* of solving the problem, solutions, and different ways of expressing solutions to the problem also lend themselves to brainstorming.

Here is a typical word problem from the intermediate grades of the elementary school: Farmer Randy Perkins has 13 animals in his farmyard. There are 5 stalls or cubicles in his barn. Farmer Perkins wants to put the same number of animals in each stall. How many animals should he put in each stall?

Jim Wadsworth, a fourth-grade teacher, and his class read the word problem about Farmer Perkins together. Imagine that you are the teacher. What ramifications and interpretations do you see in the word problem just stated? Discuss *many* methods of solving the problem and identify *many* ways of expressing an answer to the problem.

The authors would like to restate the generalization that in teaching mathematics, teachers tend to emphasize "the correct answer" instead of presenting problems that are open-ended in nature. This presentation of closure acts to stifle creativity in students.

When I was a student, I studied under a great lecturer and a great teacher. The great lecturer gave marvelously clear and witty lectures in which he gave the answers to problems he had solved long ago. Since they were already solved they were not our problems, and we forgot the answers on our way out of the examination room. The great teacher was a poor lecturer, but he came in and talked about problems he hadn't been able to solve. We tried to help him and have been different people ever since.[1]

Elementary-school children should be guided so that they come face-to-face, not with stone walls, but with areas of mathematics that offer horizons for problem-solving.

Mathematical Problems for Brainstorming

Creative people like to consider many alternatives when solving problems. Class brainstorming is one method of encouraging children to do this. One way the teacher can promote flexible problem-solving is to demonstrate some examples.

Here are a few mathematical problems that you can read to your class in a serious tone of voice. Have your class try to compute the answer to each problem; then read the answer that is "correct." The answers will tickle the children's funny bones and at the same time help them realize that any mathematical word problem has many ramifications. You and your pupils may want to brainstorm a series of answers to each of the problems. This process can be great fun and can "loosen up" rigid thinking.

"UNTWIST IT!"

Problem: Henry Smith went to the grocery store with a shopping list prepared by his wife, telling him to buy two cans of peaches, a large loaf of white bread and two dozen eggs. The peaches cost 35 cents a can, the bread was 28 cents, and the eggs were two dozen for $1.19. How much did Mr. Smith spend?

Answer: $9.21. He bought two cans of peaches, a loaf of pumpernickel, three cans of smoked oysters, a pound of imported cheese and a case of soda pop. He forgot the eggs.

Problem: There are five people in a family. Three of them wear a clean pair of socks every day; one changes his socks three times a week; one changes socks twice a day. How many socks will there be in the weekly wash?

Answer: You never know. At least three socks will have no mates.

[1] Donald Snygg, "The Fully Functioning Person," *Current Issues in Higher Education* (Washington, D.C.: Association for Higher Education, 1963).

Problem: If a child walks 1½ blocks in 4½ minutes, how long will it take him to walk 30 blocks?
Answer: No self-respecting child would dream of walking 30 blocks. He'd insist on being driven in the car.[2]

Creativity and Basic Problem-solving Behaviors

Research indicates that creative people are unusually enthusiastic and skillful problem-solvers. In fact, it is the creative person's facility and flexibility in handling problems that in most instances sets him apart from the average human being. The ability to entertain and examine a wider scope of solutions to problems appears to be one type of special "magic" which creative people possess. Many experts feel that there are different kinds of creativity and that this affects the manner in which problem-solving is approached. Some also propose that creative behavior involves a lot more than unique problem-solving behavior. Perhaps this is true. But let us examine the four phases of problem-solving commonly identified by psychologists. And let us examine them in relation to how creative people often deal with them.

The Four Phases of Problem-Solving

PHASE ONE: *recognition and definition of a problem; relation to problem; sometimes called the exposure stage.* This first phase of problem-solving may be the actual pulse of creativity. It may be the single factor that sets the highly creative person apart. Creative people seem to be supersensitized to the recognition of problems. Many times this supersensitivity applies to problems in a particular area, such as electronics, oil painting, or music. But there are highly creative individuals who seem to have the ability to identify more problems than the average person does in whatever area they find themselves.

Since the creative person views the world as unfinished, incomplete, needing much improvement, he is quick to identify the problematic aspects of almost everything in his immediate environment. He identifies problems and needed change where others fail to see them. He sees problems within problems.

PHASE TWO: *fact-finding or incubation stage.* Creative individuals

[2] Jane Goodsell, "Untwist It!" (575 Lexington Avenue, New York 22, N.Y.: *The American Weekly,* July 16, 1961).

seek out and select the facts they believe necessary to solve the problem on which they are working. Very often they will seem to ignore existing facts in seeking a solution to a problem. An awareness of a great number of facts relative to a problem area may inhibit an individual's creativity, which is often said to begin where the facts leave off. In mathematics, it may be inhibiting to the individual who wants to create a new system of numeration to possess a great deal of information about the existing systems. Then again, for another person attacking the same task, it may be important to be aware of existing systems. The role of facts in the creative process escapes definition. A mathematician seeking to create a design for a new computer may be inhibited by a vast knowledge of existing electronic circuitry or of existing computer design. The role of facts in the creative process appears to be relative to the nature of the individual engaging in the creative process and the nature of the particular task being undertaken. What little research we have available as to the utilization of facts in the creative process indicates that highly creative individuals

1. Tend to see more and different relationships and/or interpretations among facts than persons of average creative abilities.
2. Are less apt to accept facts as being absolute facts.
3. Frequently ignore existing facts and select a solution or course of action which appears to be in opposition to known facts.

PHASE THREE: *hypothesizing; experimenting; illumination.* Following the collection of needed facts, the creative problem-solver in mathematics, or in any other area, begins to search for a self-satisfying solution through hypothesizing. The hypothesizing stage of creativity is undoubtedly the most puzzling—the most unexplainable. It involves spurious, unpredictable behavior on the part of the highly creative individual. He may hypothesize a solution to the problem which appears to be irrelevant to the facts. Intuition, feelings, and a personal whim may give stronger direction to the creative problem-solver than logical deductive reasoning.

During the hypothesizing stage, the highly creative person has the advantage of being able to explore mentally a much wider range of possible solutions than can the person of average creative ability. Consequently, the final selection of a solution will have come from a broader realm or map of hypotheses.

PHASE FOUR: *selection, verification, and elaboration of a solution or solutions.* This phase is explained in Chapter 7, which deals with an examination of the steps of the discovery method and/or process.

Creativity and the Discovery Method

The "discovery" method of teaching has been closely associated with arithmetic and mathematics for several decades. A major share of present teaching methods books relative to mathematics contain descriptions of the discovery method and its importance as a method of teaching. The discovery method is not a complex idea but a very basic and logical one. Yet at one period in the evolution of educational pedagogy in the United States, this method of teaching was viewed as revolutionary. It represented a radical departure from existing teaching methods. Although the discovery method rode into general acceptance on the wave of the progressive education movement in the early thirties, it is not a child of progressive education. Its basic principle dates back to the dawn of learning. Early man employed a type of "discovery learning" when he investigated his immediate environment. He discovered how to hollow out a stone or piece of wood to use as a bowl. He discovered how to use an animal skin for warmth. His discovery was of a random nature, but discovering *can* be made *deliberate* and organized.

What Is the Discovery Method of Teaching Mathematics?

The discovery method of teaching embraces a set of procedures through which a teacher guides his class to the desired outcomes. These procedures constitute a "method" of discovering answers to a problem. The discovery method is not solely applicable to the teaching of mathematics but is often employed in social studies, science, etc., as well. If the reader will compare the description of the discovery method that follows with the general steps of problem-solving described in Chapter 7, he will find general congruency.

The discovery method of teaching involves four basic steps as diagrammed in Figure 7–2.

*   *   *

Now let us examine a specific lesson illustrating the employment of the "discovery method" in teaching mathematics. Miss Gormon, as an on-going part of her classroom mathematics program, plans to help her fifth-grade group "discover" a method of computation relative to the multiplication of fractions. More specifically, she wants her students to discover the fact that multiplying the numerators and denominators of two fractions will yield a product efficiently and accurately. As the introduction and motivating device for the lesson,

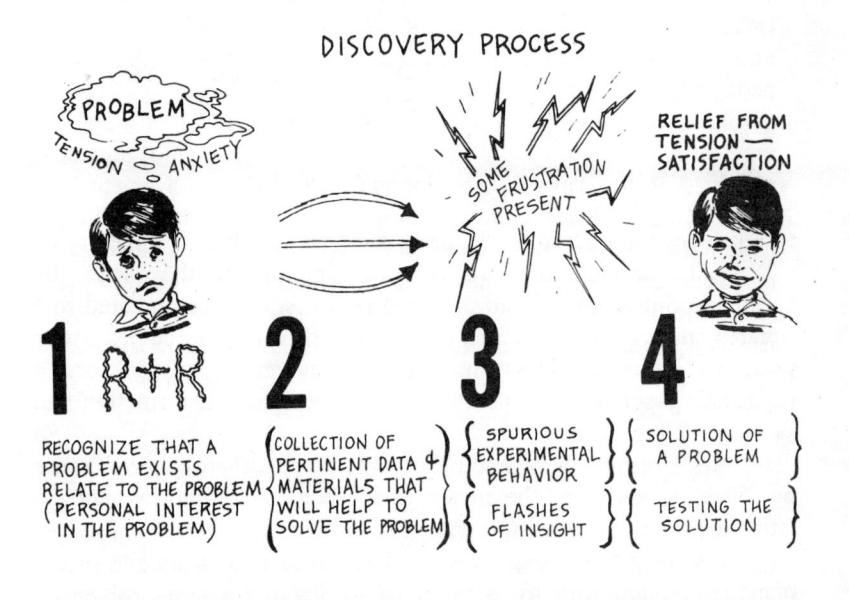

FIGURE 7–2. *Four basic steps in the discovery method*

she tells a story about some children and their need to find ½ of ½. She uses a flannel board with cardboard cut-outs as visual materials to help the story come alive for the children. The children are encouraged to experiment with scissors and paper at their desks in an attempt to depict the answer by demonstrating ½ of ½. Miss Gormon restates the problem on which the class is working: "How can we find an answer to one-half of one-half?" By cutting one half of a piece of paper in half, the child is able to show (demonstrate) what the answer "looks like."

Miss Gormon assists her class in determining what equal part of the whole sheet the ½ of ½ represents. It is necessary to compare the piece of paper which represents ½ of ½ with the original whole sheet (shown in Figure 7–3). Through conversation the children are led to conclude that the ½ of ½ is equal to ¼ of the whole sheet. Then a *number sentence* is constructed by Miss Gormon and her class

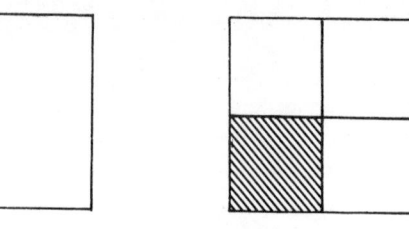

SHADED AREA INDICATES
½ OF ½

FIGURE 7–3. *One half of one half*

to represent the operation: ½ of ½ = ¼ or ½ taken ½ times = ¼.

While the children were experimenting to find the answer by cutting up differently shaped pieces of paper, several commented that squares and rectangles seemed easier to work with than circles. After some discussion, the class finally agreed that given only scissors, a ruler, and paper, it was difficult to work with circles if a fraction like ⅓ was called for.

Miss Gormon then posed the question, "Is there some manner by which we could find the answer to one-half of one-half by manipulating the fractions as written symbols?"

"It's going to be rough if we all have to carry scissors and pieces of paper around with us in order to work out fraction problems," one boy in the class commented. The class enjoyed his humor.

"Well, we know from cutting the paper that one-half taken one-half times is one-quarter, or one-half of one-half equals one-quarter," Miss Gormon recapitulated for the class. She wrote ½ of ½ = ¼ on the greenboard. "Study this algorism for a few minutes and be ready to suggest some method of operating with just the written symbols in order to arrive at the answer."

The students studied the algorism. After a quiet period Miss Gormon called for suggestions (hypotheses). "I'll write down your suggestions here on the greenboard," she said, "and then we can attempt to determine how functional each hypothesis is."

The suggestions that came from the students were these:

1. Add the denominators (2 + 2) and carry over the common numerators (1). This gives the answer: ¼.
2. Multiply the numerators and then multiply the denominators (1 × 1 and 2 × 2).

3. Multiply the numerators (1×1) and add the two denominators together $(2 + 2)$.

Much excitement is generated among the students, as they are anxious to test and verify one or more of the hypotheses. The class discusses various plans of action.

"First we'll need some fractional algorisms to apply the hypotheses to," one student suggests. The class agrees and the students compose a group of several algorisms, deliberately including one algorism whose denominator and numerator differ. Part of the class elects to verify the answer to each algorism, using cut paper. Others choose to apply one or more of the three hypotheses the class is testing. The work of the students will result in identifying which of the hypotheses, if any, is applicable universally, and which, if any, are applicable in a restricted manner.

Miss Gormon's class will have "discovered" one or more methods of multiplying fractions. Testing out the reliability of their "discoveries" will take several more days.

If Miss Gormon and her students are working on an algorism such as $24 + 13 + 19 + 30 = ?$, they still discuss the algorism together before attempting to compute the answer, just as they would discuss a mathematical word problem. "What are some other ways in which we could write this algorism?" Miss Gormon asks. Her students suggest many alternatives (brainstorming). Some of the suggestions are as follows:

$(24 + 13) + (19 + 30) = ?$

Tens	Ones
2	4
1	3
1	9
3	0

$$20 + 4$$
$$10 + 3$$
$$20 - 1$$
$$+ 30$$

Ancient Egyptian notation

Binary

∩∩ IIII
∩ III
∩ III
III
III

∩∩∩

11000
1101
10011
+ 11110

Should the Conventional Conception of the Discovery Method Be Modified?

The authors are convinced that the general framework of the conventional discovery method is positively correlated with the promotion of creative thinking. This method of teaching, if somewhat modified in its implementation, can be highly conducive to the promotion of creative problem-solving. We suggest that changes need to be made in the conventional implementation of the discovery method. What, specifically, are they?

The first area or step, as you may recall, involves the identification and recognition of the problem. The teacher and students discuss the nature of the mathematical word problem or algorism being considered. Whereas teachers of mathematics have tended to promote a *narrow* description of mathematical problems, the teacher who desires to promote creativity in mathematics must lead her students to take a broader, more flexible view of the problem. One of the characteristics of highly creative people is that they are more sensitive in assessing the scope of problems. Creative people tend to see problems *within* a problem, which others do not. They identify related, tangential problems more readily.

The authors suggest that more time and emphasis be given to classroom experiences aimed at promoting in students the abilities concomitant with viewing mathematical problems flexibly.

The second step of the conventional discovery method is the one that is most controversial in terms of its relationship to creative thinking. It consists of lead-up or channeling activities, which are usually directed by the teacher. The purpose is to confront students with some experiences (data) which they (the students) can use as cues to form a generalization. For example, suppose the teacher wants his students to "discover" the mathematical principle that *the order of the addends does not affect the sum.* He could present some classroom activities of a lead-up nature that would exemplify this principle. But what kind and how many? The best answer seems to be that the need varies with each child. There are many children who do not need to experience deliberately staged lead-up activities or cues to "discover" that the order of the addends does not affect the sum; they could discover it in a laissez-faire type of setting. Many educators who are highly sensitized to the promotion of creativity hold the position that *any* lead-up activities or cues are inhibiting to creative thinking. They argue that lead-up activities, no matter how subtle, serve to channel students' creative thinking toward one or two predetermined outcomes. On the other hand, opponents of this argument point out that the entire school program, including the curriculum, can be considered as being in opposition to the development of creative thinking in children. But as long as we place students in the general structure of a classroom environment, teacher-guided learning experiences for children are insurance against the chaos that could grow out of laissez-faire settings.

In summation, step two of the discovery method is ultrasensitive in terms of its effects upon the development of creativity in children. Some children need lead-up activities in order to "discover" a mathematical principle in a meaningful way. But other more creative students may want to develop their own lead-up activities through independent experimentation.

Step three of the discovery method may well constitute the essence of the creative process. This is the point when the students are turned loose to propose and select solutions to the problem, when they carry out experimental behavior in an attempt to create order out of chaos.

This area is shrouded in great mystery; neither educators nor psychologists are able to describe accurately the mental processes involved. We do know that at this time students do experience flashes of insight and make intuitive leaps to step four of the discovery method. But we do not really know how.

Step three is that point at which human magic enters the scene. The human brain is capable of producing an unbelievable number of answers to any given mathematical situation if prodded to do so. Consequently, the teacher's role here should be mainly that of an encouraging bystander. To the teacher of mathematics the authors offer this advice: Observe. Make suggestions when asked to. Encourage the frustrated one to press on to a solution. Be open and permissive in tolerating what may appear at times to be nonconstructive behavior.

We know that the character of the immediate environment of the creative person can drastically affect his ability to exercise his creativity. The classroom can be very inhibiting to some students working at level three; therefore the teacher should frequently assign work at this level as homework.

The time element in step three is also an unpredictable and capricious element. Some students may appear to accomplish this stage within a matter of seconds, while others may continue to wrestle with possible solutions for hours, days, and, in some cases, for years. Who knows when the subconscious mind completely "writes off" a challenging problem? Step three, the ideation step, will take different forms with different individuals. Traditionally, teachers have tended to become impatient with students if they did not come up with glib, immediate responses. Be patient with this process. Let us give students more take-home problems to which they can apply long-term thinking.

The teacher of mathematics needs to encourage and entertain hospitably students' suggestions for alternate roads to mathematical problem-solving.

Invention may be precluded by a distrust of deviation. Every new and good thing is liable to seem eccentric and perhaps dangerous at first glimpse, perhaps more than what is really eccentric, really irrelevant to life. And therefore we must always listen to the voice of eccentricity, within ourselves and in the world. The alien, the dangerous, like the negligible near thing, may seem irrelevant to purpose and yet the call to our own fruitful development. This does not mean that we should surrender to whatever novelty is brought to attention. It does mean that we must practice to some extent an imaginative surrender to every novelty that has even the most tenuous credentials. Because life is larger than any of its expressions, it must sometimes do violence to the forms it has created.[3]

The fourth step of the discovery method, the reader may recall, involves the selection of a solution to the mathematical problem. It also involves testing and evaluating the selected solution. Step four is as delicate as a snowflake. It is so easy to unconsciously promote *one* (the teacher's) solution to the mathematical algorism being considered. Step four needs to be dealt with in a fluid manner if it is to contribute to the development of creative thinking and the evolution of a creative solution that is the brainchild of the *students* involved.

Teachers often have one absolute solution which they want the students to parrot; they tend to respond favorably to students who produce the one "right" answer. But step four needs rather to be perceived as a configuration or galaxy of acceptable responses from children. These should include: (1) many methods of working the problem, (2) many answers and methods of recording the answer, and (3) many methods for checking and verifying the answers.

[3] Brewster Ghiselin, *The Creative Process* (Berkeley, Calif.: University of California Press, 1952), p. 31.

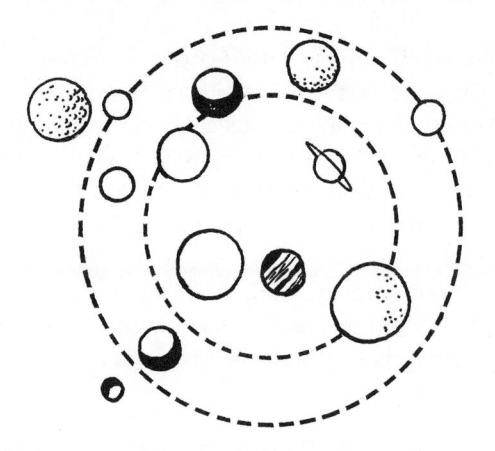

FIGURE 7–4. *A galaxy of acceptable student responses*

One of the greatest strengths of the so-called new math programs lies in their fluid approach to step four of the "discovery process." Teachers are encouraged to employ questions similar to these: "How many ways can we express a solution to the problem?" "What do *you* see as a solution to the problem, John?" "Does anyone see another way of notating the solution that Gail has suggested?" "How can we check the accuracy of Peter's solution to the problem?" "Can anyone think of another way to state the generalization we have developed?"

These questions and many more like them are used by mathematics teachers who desire to promote a flexible and creative attitude in their students in relation to expressing solutions to a problem.

* * *

The numerical solution to a problem in Miss Cassell's second grade was 12. How many ways can we write the number 12? The suggestions begin slowly from the class, but then one student's idea triggers a related idea in another student's mind. Miss Cassell records the students' suggestions on the greenboard. A few of these are as follows: (10 + 2); twelve; 1100 (binary); (15 − 3); (3 × 4); (9 + 2 + 1).

"How many ways do you suppose there *are* for expressing the number twelve?" Miss Cassell asks her students. A lively class discussion follows. Billy suggests that maybe there are an "uncountable" number of ways to express the quantity of 12. Miss Cassell interjects the term "infinite number of ways" as another way of stating Billy's idea.

More discussion ensues. Miss Cassell is encouraging a flexible manner of expressing mathematical ideas. In addition to promoting flexible mathematical notation, a teacher who would promote creativity in students should encourage them to produce a galaxy of solutions to any mathematical problem. Often a child may suggest a solution to a problem, and if it is not "the one" given in the teacher's manual the teacher will not accept the answer for examination. All answers or solutions which children sincerely suggest to a mathematical problem should be placed "in the hopper" to be evaluated by the class and defined by the child who suggested it.

* * *

In Miss Thomas' fourth grade one group in mathematics read this word problem: Tony spent 45¢ for paint and 40¢ for colored pencils. How much money did he spend for these things? The group of students worked independently on the answer, each using a personal plan of attack. As soon as each child was able to produce an answer, he wrote his answer on a small piece of paper and deposited it in the "answer hopper" (a small cardboard box) sitting on the floor. Each student in the group was encouraged to submit *one or more* solutions.

After students had made the contributions to the "answer hopper," the group leader opened the hopper and read each one. The group was encouraged to question and/or discuss any answer that had been submitted; they finally decided upon one or more answers that had proven to be accurate.

Ninety percent of the answers to the problem listed the quantity 85¢ in some form. The group discussed the fact that it could be written in many ways: $.85; $\frac{85}{100}$; 85¢; eighty-five cents, etc.

There were several answers that were incorrect. One was 95¢; the group identified this answer as being inaccurate. The group member who submitted it was invited to defend it if he so desired. He stated he had added wrong. The group accepted this in a matter-of-fact manner. One answer to the question was 87¢. The student who submitted this answer explained that there is a 2 percent state sales tax in effect and that Tony would have to pay it. The group decided that the answer was certainly a possibility but since the problem did not state where the sale took place the tax factor could not be figured into the solution.

Another answer said "less than 85¢." The child explained that if trading stamps were given with the sale the local sales price would be diminished by the value of the stamps. The group agreed that this was a variable they had not thought about but that since there was no information given in the problem relative to trading stamps, the answer was "unprovable" though in the realm of possibility. Miss Thomas' math group is showing evidence of probing the limits of a problem.

Why Is the Discovery Method Important to Creative Problem-solving?

The authors have allocated considerable space to the discovery method of teaching mathematics. The authors are convinced that the mechanics of the discovery method constitute the general framework of creative problem-solving. Consciously or not, every individual who attempts to solve a problem progresses through some of the steps of the discovery method. In fact, the term *discovery* may be the most accurate description of creativity that will ever be evolved. Creativity *is* discovery—discovery of one's self and one's ability to respond uniquely to a stimulus. The stimulus or problem involved may be the blank canvas that confronts the painter, a rough chunk of granite that stands before the sculptor, or the need of a musician to find a manner in which to convey a particular feeling or sensation. The term *problem* as used here is intended to mean anything that stimulates need-fulfillment in the learner.

The strong emphasis placed upon the role of the discovery method in promoting creativity in the teaching of mathematics does not deny a place to other methods of teaching mathematics. The lecture and discussion methods may trigger off the identification of problems in the minds of students. Once a problem is identified and found meaningful by the students, they may engage in creative problem-solving. But the lecture method and the discussion method of presenting mathematics serve best as springboards to creative thinking. Neither method has the mechanics of individual problem-solving inherent in its structure, as does the discovery method. Rather, these methods can serve as teaching techniques for presenting mathematics to students where individual problem-solving is not a *primary* objective of the particular mathematics lesson.

In summary, *all* individuals who engage in creative problem-solving utilize steps of the discovery method. It is true that many highly creative problem-solvers may skip one or more of the steps in the discovery process. And sometimes a creative problem-solver, whether it be the mathematics teacher or his students, will go through the steps of the discovery process in reverse order. For example, a student, after recognizing a mathematics problem, may have a "hunch" as to the correct answer without any data-gathering. This means that he has jumped from step one of the discovery process directly to step four. Then, after he decides his answer is probably an accurate one (step four), he may decide to go back to steps two and three and check the validity and accuracy of his answer.

Highly creative people who report the mechanics of their own creative process, including ideation, consistently describe the basic steps of the discovery process. The language employed in the reporting is quite diverse, and some of them appear to be much more conscious of their creative acts than others. But, generally speaking, they report their creativity as *discovery*.

The authors refer the reader to the reports of highly creative persons that appear in *The Creative Process,* Brewster Ghiselin, ed., University of California Press, Berkeley, California, 1952.

Mathematics Goes Automotive!

A creative teacher guiding a group of children down the main street of mathematics explores many side streets as well, since, being creative, she is apt to see more relationships between mathematics and other areas of the curriculum. As a result, mathematics is frequently taught in conjunction with social studies, science, art, music.

* * *

Judy Kirby, a sixth-grade teacher, noticed that her class seemed to possess an unusual interest in automobiles. This was particularly true of the boys in the class, many of whom had assembled plastic models of automobiles from commercial kits. She decided to capitalize upon this keen interest in order to accomplish some specific educational objectives.

Since it was the fall of the year, the local automobile dealers were featuring their new models. Miss Kirby visited each auto dealer and secured from them some very attractive and colorful advertising brochures, which they were happy to supply free of charge. Miss Kirby made certain that she gave each auto dealer the opportunity to contribute some material.

The next day the class discussed the automobile brochures that Miss Kirby had collected. They decided to cut out various sections of the brochures and mount them on large pieces of colored oak tag.

Many principles of art were discussed in conjunction with mounting the brochure material in an attractive fashion. Some posters had colored pictures of the interiors of the new automobiles; others featured pictures of grillwork, motors, body profiles, etc. There was so much material that when it was mounted all of the classroom walls were covered. Some of the girls and boys in the class decided to study the basic shapes of new automobiles in terms of their wind resistance; this project led them to the construction of a simple yet workable wind tunnel. Another group was studying the color combinations and textures used in the interiors of the new autos. Two boys compared the design and functionality of instrument panels.

The class composed original songs, stories, and poems about automobiles in keeping with the classroom "autorama." Mathematics was constantly in focus throughout the week and a half. The different sizes of wheel base were discussed and compared mathematically. Engine horsepower was defined and mathematical comparisons made. Several groups of students composed mathematical word problems dealing with automobiles. Mileage and speed problems were prevalent.

Much science was integrated into the study of automobiles. Other classes in the school were invited to Miss Kirby's room to experience a visual and verbal presentation of the autorama. The children in Miss Kirby's class were having an interdisciplinary learning experience in which mathematics played an important part.

Creative Mathematics Assignments

Open-ended mathematics assignments are not easy to derive from the vantage point of the teacher. Deliberate lead-up work is usually a prerequisite to the actual assignment that is designed to foster creativity. Let us look at the method and factual information involved in developing one such open-ended assignment.

* * *

Miss Alice Jackson's fifth grade has been studying the history of the Hindu-Arabic number system. The activity began when one member of the class asked a question about the origin of counting: How did people long ago keep track of how many things they had? Did they write numbers down on paper like we do today? Did they have any simple machines to help them? These and several other questions led to a search of reference books.

Miss Jackson's class collected and catalogued factual information about the evolution of counting. They learned that primitive counting or tallying took many forms. They discussed the idea of one-to-one correspondence, which incorporates associating one counter with one object to be counted. Early man used pebbles as counters to establish one-to-one correspondence. Some children showed examples of knotted rope or vine used as a tallying device. Notched sticks and finger counting, two other varieties of early counting devices, were identified and discussed.

Miss Jackson and her class discussed and evaluated the strengths and weaknesses of several counting devices. The class was led to reiterate the purposes of these devices. Many of the children thought that they could improve upon the primitive counting devices that had been considered. Since there seemed to be general group interest in this activity, Miss Jackson recognized it as an opportunity to develop an open-ended type of assignment for her class to encourage creativity. And so, with her class, Miss Jackson formulated the general description of the homework task. Each class member, or two class members working together, was challenged to develop some type of counting or tallying device and demonstrate it for the class. The class decided that they would need several days in order to give this task proper attention.

Ideas began popping up in the informal conversation among children. Without being aware of the name for it, some of the children were brainstorming possible devices that could be used. A few days later counting devices began appearing in the classroom.

Sandy Dennis displayed and demonstrated a counter employing a muffin tin and colored buttons.

Ralph St. Angels contributed another type of counting device. On a piece of plywood 10 by 12 inches he had smeared a one-quarter-inch layer of plasticene (a type of clay that does not harden). With a wooden stick, counting marks can be made in the clay; then, after each counting exercise, the clay board can be smoothed over, which in effect erases the board. There are three colors of clay on the board. Ralph explains that each color represents a different power of 12. Ralph's idea is a modification of the ancient dust boards, sand tables, or clay tablets used for recording mathematical computation.

In reporting and demonstrating the results of their creative efforts, Ricky and Bruce, two class members, showed an electronic counter they had constructed. It was made by using a piece of peg board, four dry cell batteries, switches, wire, and some small flashlight bulbs. A graphic representation of their creative efforts can be seen in Figure 11–14.

And so one by one the many counting devices were demonstrated and discussed by Miss Jackson's class. Because of its open-ended nature, the assignment offered each member of the class an opportunity to innovate in an individual manner. It is obvious that this type of problem-solving assignment encourages children's creativity. Did this assignment in any way indicate creative thinking on the part of Miss Jackson, the teacher?

 *** Modulus, Murals, and Measurement**

Mathematics possesses not only truth, but supreme beauty—a beauty cold and austere, like that of sculpture, without appeal to any part of our weaker nature, sublimely pure, and capable of a stern perfection such as only the greatest art can show.

BERTRAND RUSSELL (1872–   )

Modular or Clock Arithmetic

Modular arithmetic can be said to run around in circles. In fact, modular arithmetic is often called clock arithmetic because it is cyclic in nature. Modular arithmetic involves number systems that employ a limited number of units and then repeat themselves. It can help to promote creative expression in students as well as foster other educational objectives. It can be used as a basic idea from which children may be able to "hitchhike" a variation of the modular idea.

Why Include Modular Arithmetic in the Elementary School Mathematics Curriculum?

The justifications for inclusion of modular arithmetic in a modern mathematics program at the elementary school level are numerous. Most noteworthy are the following: (1) There are many examples of modular number systems that reside in our society—days of the week, months of the year, the clocks that tell us the time of day. (2) Modular arithmetic can be used as a system for checking addition, subtraction, multiplication, and division computation in our decimal system. (3) Because a modular number system operates within limits, it makes basic mathematics principles less complex to demonstrate to children. A modular number system is not as unwieldy as our open-ended decimal system.

* Eight in Hebrew.

By employing a modular number system, a teacher can help children to discover and examine the mechanics of the four basic processes within defined limits, analogous to placing the processes under a microscope.

A modular arithmetic system employs a limited number of symbols. For example, let us consider a modulus five (mod 5) system. Since we have chosen a mod 5 system, we can use only five symbols and five corresponding units to express all counting numbers. As the five symbols, let us use 0, 1, 2, 3, 4. In Figure 8–1 the reader may observe a portion of two number lines: a conventional number line (base 10) and a mod 5 number line. Both number lines begin at zero and proceed to the equivalent of the counting number 12.

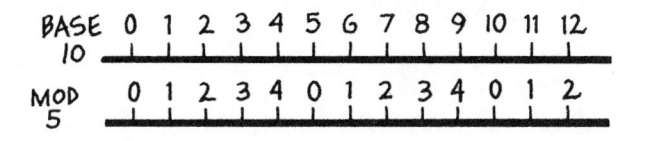

FIGURE 8–1. *Two number lines*

From the mod 5 number line the reader can observe that a modular number system uses the same symbols in a repetitive manner to designate counting numbers. The numeral 6 in mod 5 is represented by a 1 if we begin with zero. (Refer to a dictionary for a literal definition of the term *modulus*.)

Another method of conceiving a mod system, in addition to the horizontal number line, is to depict the units of such a system in a circular or clock-like manner. Figure 8–2 shows a mod 5 clock. Notice that while the clock has 5 equal units, the largest numeral on the clock is 4. It is a mod 5 clock because it consists of 5 equal units depicted by 5 different numerals. The numeral 5 could be substituted for the zero on the clock, as the numeral 0 serves as both zero and 5. This is not illogical; one numeral on any clock serves as the beginning and the end of the circular system. On the conventional clock that we all know, the 12 serves not only as 12 but also as zero, because we begin counting hours from that point.

To develop curiosity in students about a modulus number system, the teacher may elect to use many techniques. Frequently a rather direct confrontation with a sample of modulus computation is effective. One teacher told his class that he was going to show them a

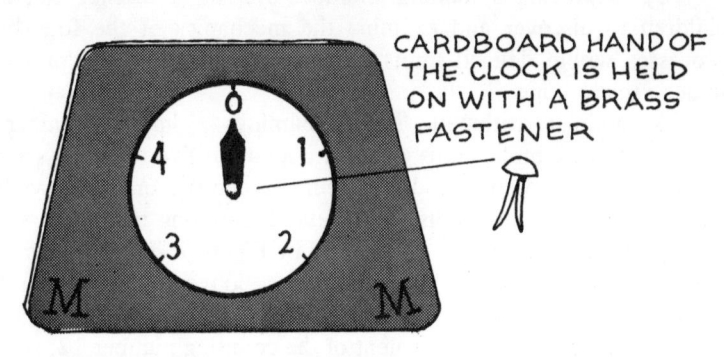

CARDBOARD HAND OF THE CLOCK IS HELD ON WITH A BRASS FASTENER

MODULUS FIVE CLOCK--MADE FROM HEAVY CARDBOARD

FIGURE 8–2. *Mod 5 clock*

strange yet accurate answer to a familiar number sentence. On the greenboard he wrote $4 + 2 = 1$. The students looked puzzled and began whispering and mumbling among themselves. How could that number sentence be true? The teacher chuckled a bit and went on to say that the number sentence he had just written on the greenboard was true when projected into a mod 5 number system. "Modulus five number system. What's that?" came the reply. Many children in the class were then ready and eager to investigate this new horizon called "modulus arithmetic."

Mod 5

Let us examine the number sentence written in mod 5 which was used by the teacher: $4 + 2 = 1$. To prove the answer, use the mod 5 number lines shown in Figure 8–1 or the mod 5 clock shown in Figure 8–2. Begin at 0 on either the number line or mod clock and count 5 units. Be sure you count clockwise on the mod clock. After counting 4 units from 0 count 2 more units *beyond* 4. This places the hand of the clock on numeral 1; likewise, it places your marker on the mod 5 number line at 1. Therefore, in the mod 5 number system, 4 plus 2 equals 1.

John's mother needs to do some shopping. At 11 A.M. she asks her son John to wait at home until she returns. She says, "I will be back in three hours." Three hours added to 11 o'clock means that

John's mother will return from shopping at about 2 o'clock. Another way of recording the number work is like this: 11 o'clock plus three hours more becomes 2 o'clock.

Do you mean to say that 11 plus 3 equals 2? Strange answers begin to appear when one applies the basic processes of addition, subtraction, multiplication, and division to a circular (modular) number system.

Using the mod 5 clock, find the sum in each of the following examples:

Base 10		Mod 5	Base 10		Mod 5
5 + 2	=	?	10 + 3	=	?
6 + 8	=	?	21 + 7	=	?
9 + 3	=	?	16 + 5	=	?

If need be, prove your answers to the examples above by demonstrating each example on a mod 5 clock you have constructed.

Making a Set of Mod 5 Cards

A set of mod 5 cards can be used in place of, or in conjunction with, the mod 5 clock. These cards can help students to check their answers to mod 5 algorisms. A simple set of mod cards is shown in Figure 8–3. They can be increased or decreased in number to coincide

FIGURE 8–3. *Set of mod cards*

with the particular modulus system you desire to demonstrate. A large set of mod cards may be useful to the teacher in demonstrating modulus operations for students. It may be wise to encourage all students in the class to construct mod cards or a mod clock to use as an individual manipulative device. As shown in Figure 8–4, a paper picnic plate, a cardboard hand, and a brass fastener can be used by students to make a modulus clock for manipulation at their desks.

FIGURE 8–4. *Mod 8 clock made from a paper plate*

Any number but 0 and 1 can be employed to determine the size of the modulus system. Why are 0 and 1 excluded?

Employing the Mod 5 Cards

As a general introduction to the utilization of mod cards, children first should learn to count with them. First, each student stacks his mod 5 cards "in order," which results in the 4 card being on the bottom and the 0 card on top.

To count forward with the mod 5 cards, the student takes a card from the top of the stack and places it on the bottom. Counting with mod 5 cards teaches the student to ascertain the numeral in mod 5 that is equivalent to the numeral given in base 10.

3 in base 10 is equivalent to   ?   in mod 5
9 in base 10 is equivalent to   4   in mod 5
21 in base 10 is equivalent to   ?   in mod 5

When students can do simple counting with the cards they are ready to work on addition algorisms. One addition task that can be presented is having the students determine the basic addition facts using mod 5. How many different addition combinations can be made with five symbols? After discussing and demonstrating one or two of the basic addition facts (such as $3 + 4 = 2$ and $4 + 4 = 3$) the students can be set free to figure out the remaining sums. (If you are not familiar with the term *basic facts,* refer to Chapter 3.) Remember that to add with the cards you move them one at a time from the top to the bottom.

To add 4 + 4 in mod 5 the student begins by checking to see that his cards are stacked in order. Then he moves the 0 card from the top of the stack to the bottom. He does the same thing with the 1, 2, and 3 cards. This leaves the 4 card on top of the stack. Now the student has counted to 4, but the algorism calls for 4 + 4. This means that he should take 4 more cards from the top of the deck and place them on the bottom. The card that is left on top of the stack after this is done is the 3 card; therefore 4 + 4 = 3. On the mod 5 clock the 4 + 4 algorism is demonstrated by moving the hand of the clock as indicated in Figure 8–5.

FIGURE 8–5. *The 4 + 4 algorism on the mod 5 clock*

Inside-Out Addition

The subtraction process can be conveniently portrayed as the inverse of the addition process by using a mod clock, mod cards, or a modulus number line. Most children should be able to figure out for themselves how to demonstrate the subtraction process with the mod materials. To subtract 2 from 4 on a mod clock, begin with the hand of the clock on 4 and move it backward (counterclockwise) two units. This places the hand at 2. Therefore 4 minus 2 in mod 5 is 2.

If he uses the mod cards, the student should count with them to 4, because this is the number with which we begin. Once this is done, the 4 card is on top of the stack. Then, to subtract with the cards, the student should move them from the bottom of the deck to the top. This, of course, is just the opposite of addition. And it is one time when it is correct to "deal from the bottom of the deck." Counting backward two cards from the 4 card places the 2 card on top. This means that $4 - 2 = 2$ in mod 5.

On the mod 5 number line, begin at 4 and count backward on the number line two marks. The point at which you arrive is 2.

Using a mod 5 manipulative device (clock, cards, or number line) work out the basic subtraction combinations for mod 5. What is the identity element for subtraction in mod 5?

Multiplication and Division in Mod 5

The relationships among the four processes can be graphically illustrated to children with modulus manipulative materials. Multiplication with the mod 5 cards, clock, or number line demonstrates the relationship between multiplication and addition, since multiplication is adding by like-size groups. For example, 4×3 is 3 added 4 times: $3 + 3 + 3 + 3$. To do this with mod cards, the children should first check to see that their cards are stacked in order (0 on top; 4 on bottom). The cards are moved top to bottom in addition; they are moved the same way in multiplication because it is a form of addition. To solve the 4×3 algorism, the student should take each card from the top and place it on the bottom of the stack while counting, "One, two, three—once; one, two, three—twice; one, two, three—three times; one, two, three—four times." If the mod clock is being employed, the student moves the hand of the clock in a clockwise direction until he has counted 3 units 4 times. The hand of the clock will come to rest on 2 ($4 \times 3 = 2$ in mod 5). Using a mod 5 number line, he simply counts forward from 0, 3 units 4 times. Figure 8–6 shows a basic fact grid for multiplication in mod 5. Fill in the products that belong in the blank spaces and verify the products that are already on the grid. What number is the identity element in multiplication using mod 5?

Division with mod 5 is the inverse of multiplication. The cards are moved from the bottom of the stack to the top; the hand on the mod clock is moved counterclockwise; the marker for the number line moves backward (toward 0). Division is related to subtraction; therefore we begin with a quantity and try to determine how many groups of a particular size we can subtract until we arrive at 0 or a remainder smaller in size than the divisor. For example, to divide 3 by 4 using the mod 5 clock, begin with the hand on 3 because the algorism asks how many 4's we can subtract from 3 *until we arrive at 0.*

FACTOR

FIGURE 8–6. *Basic fact grid for multiplication in mod 5*

Remember that the quotient in division is the number of times the divisor can be subtracted from the dividend. Work out the quotients that belong in the blank spaces on the division grid in Figure 8–7. Compare this mod 5 division grid with the multiplication grid in Figure 8–6.

Once students understand the operation of one mod system, they may be ready to develop basic fact charts using others such as mod 6, 8, 12, 15, etc.

Creativity and Modulus Arithmetic

Modulus arithmetic is a mathematical system, thus there is no particular method of teaching inherent in it. It can be presented to children in a wide variety of ways, and in this respect it is open-ended. A teacher is free to project his own method of teaching into the modulus idea.

One mod system (such as mod 5) may stimulate some students to create and explore other mod systems. They may develop variations from the basic modulus idea. Some may even want to invent

DIVIDEND

÷	0	1	2	3	4
0	0				
1			2		4
2		3			
3		2		1	
4			3		

DIVISOR

FIGURE 8–7. *Basic fact grid for division in mod 5*

audio-visual devices to demonstrate various mod systems and operations.

A third-grade youngster, after being exposed to a mod 5 number system, suggested that a number system that was some "shape" other than round might be devised. The next day he came to class with what he called his "up-and-down number system." His diagram for the number system looked like Figure 8–8, according to its eight-year-old inventor.

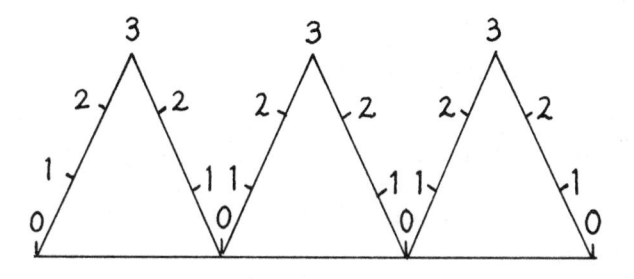

FIGURE 8–8. *The "up-and-down" number system*

He also had a list of numbers and their equivalents in his up-down number system:

Base 10

4	=	2 in up-down system
11	=	1 in up-down system
7	=	1 in up-down system

His classmates discussed the up-down system and tried out some addition and subtraction algorisms using it.

Modulus Arithmetic as a Tool for Checking Computation in Base 10

Modulus arithmetic can be employed as a quick method of checking computation in base 10. As an illustration, Figure 8–9 shows a list of prices and their sum taken from a cash register tape in a supermarket.

Of course the mod 5 check is not infallible, but it can be helpful as a speed check for column addition. A mod 5 check of a subtraction algorism is shown below:

Base 10

272 = 2 in mod 5
− 69 = 4 in mod 5

203   3

Is equal to 3   4 from 2 on the mod 5
in mod 5   clock is 3

Check: To find the mod 5 equivalent of 203 (base 10) as called for in the check shown above, divide 203 by 5. If 5 can be evenly divided into a number then the number has 0 as its equivalent in mod 5. If 5 cannot be evenly divided into a number, *the remainder* becomes the mod 5 equivalent.

Is it possible to use mod 5 to check multiplication and division computation done in base 10?

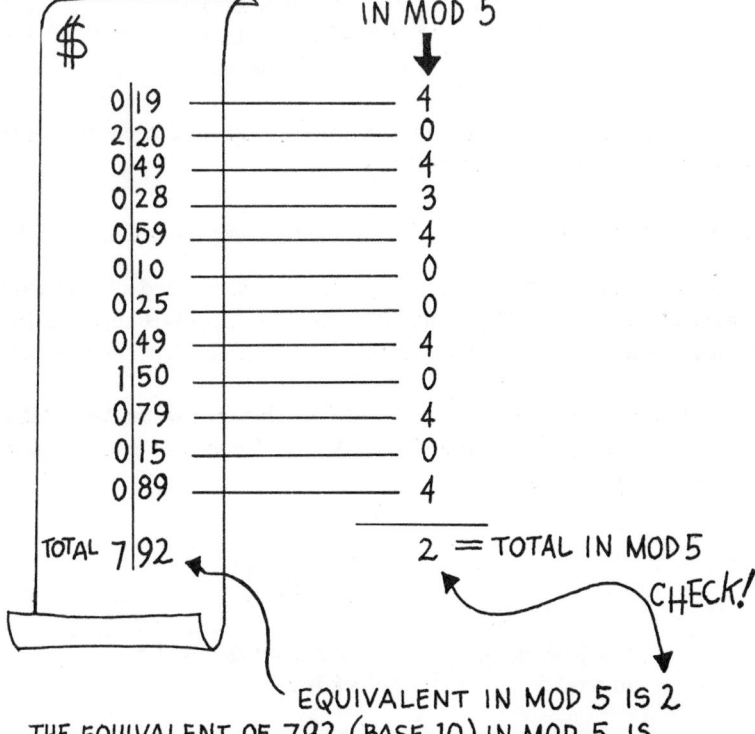

THE EQUIVALENT OF 792 (BASE 10) IN MOD 5 IS
DETERMINED BY DIVIDING 792 BY 5. THE <u>REMAINDER</u>
(2) BECOMES ITS EQUIVALENT IN MOD 5.
THE EQUIVALENT OF 792 IN MOD 5 COULD ALSO
BE DETERMINED BY MOVING THE HAND ON THE MOD
5 CLOCK AROUND AND AROUND UNTIL 792 UNITS
HAD BEEN COUNTED. THIS WOULD LEAVE THE
HAND OF THE CLOCK RESTING ON 2.

FIGURE 8–9. *The supermarket cash register tape*

Mathematics Mural?

Why, of course! Mathematics can be integrated into many art projects; it can be perceived as part of any artistic design. One characteristic of the creative teacher is that he feels free to make associations among materials and ideas. Consequently the creative teacher of mathematics helps students relate mathematics to a broad scope of seemingly unrelated areas of the curriculum. As an illustration of correlating mathematics with art, children can design murals that incorporate the principles and notations of mathematics. The mural shown in Figure 8–10, based upon the number 4, was constructed by elementary school children. It was a challenging and exciting project for them. The mural is attractive from a purely aesthetic point of view; in addition, it contains a great deal of mathematics material.

FIGURE 8–10. *Mathematics mural*

Symbols Contained in the Mathematics Mural

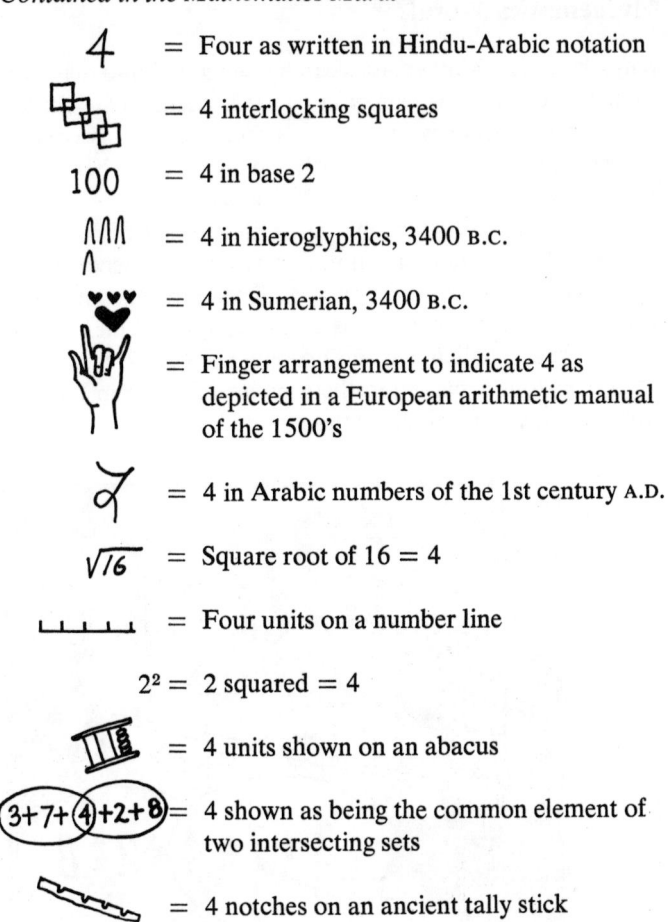

4 = Four as written in Hindu-Arabic notation

= 4 interlocking squares

100 = 4 in base 2

= 4 in hieroglyphics, 3400 B.C.

= 4 in Sumerian, 3400 B.C.

= Finger arrangement to indicate 4 as depicted in a European arithmetic manual of the 1500's

= 4 in Arabic numbers of the 1st century A.D.

$\sqrt{16}$ = Square root of 16 = 4

= Four units on a number line

2^2 = 2 squared = 4

= 4 units shown on an abacus

(3+7+④+2+8) = 4 shown as being the common element of two intersecting sets

= 4 notches on an ancient tally stick

Mathematics symbolization and notation can be incorporated into fine arts in a myriad of ways. Figure 8–11 shows a reproduction of an oil painting utilizing mathematical symbols to create an aesthetically pleasing composition. This picture was painted by a sixth-grade student who had developed a special interest in mathematics. The painting features the mathematical symbol for an inequality. The three colored circles near the top of the painting and two colored circles near the bottom illustrate this inequality. Utilizing mathematical symbols in two- or three-dimensional art activities can be an exciting challenge to students to exercise their creative abilities.

Can you think of some pieces of sculpture that are based upon mathematical patterns, symbols, principles, etc.?

FIGURE 8–11. *Mathematical symbols in oil*

A Full Measure of Measures

The emphasis in teaching children about weights and measures, whether it involves pints and quarts at the primary level or cubic measures at the intermediate level, should be to set conditions in which children have first-hand experiences *utilizing* the weights and measures. The authors suggest that the reader consult the teacher's manual accompanying any of the basic mathematics classroom textbooks in order to become familiar with the fundamental principles of presenting common weights and measures to children. Space limitations do not permit a detailed discussion of the traditional methods used. The authors choose to discuss some of the more unusual aspects of teaching weights and measures—those which are *not* traditionally included in either teachers' manuals or mathematics teaching methods books.

If the teacher desires to promote creative thinking in his students he must not only assist children to review what has been done in a mathematical area (what already is in existence), but to consider what changes, what modifications, what horizons can be sought in regard to the area. Weights and measures should be no exception.

Before attempting to apply creative thinking to weights and measures, it seems logical that students first study the evolution of our modern-day weights and measures. This study in a sense becomes the fact-finding step of the creative process. Again the authors stress that creative thinking does not occur in the absence of data—in a vacuum, so to speak.

Many children attribute the origin of weights and measures to their parents, teachers, or a book. Some even believe that a deity decreed them. In studying about the evolution of weights and measures, many children are astounded to find out that weights and measures have resulted from the ideas of men and that they (the weights and measures) have not "always been around," as one child phrased it. There are many fine classroom films and trade books available which deal with weights and measures from a mathematical as well as an historical point of view.

At one time in Europe an ox-rod was used as a measure; but farmers used ox-rods of different lengths, so this caused much strife. One rough measure of land during the medieval period was "one day's plowing." An emperor of a European country declared that the standard measure (inch) should be the length of three barley corns laid end to end. A host of ancient linear measures were derived from reference to man's body: the foot, the distance from elbow to forefinger, the width of the palm of a man's hand, etc. Children can learn from a study of the evolution of weights and measures that our standard units are the products of man's thinking and probably can be improved in many ways.

* * *

Miss Ellis' fifth grade, after reviewing standard weights and measures, decides to continue their study by tackling related specific problems as suggested by fellow-students and Miss Ellis. A question box is set up in the classroom and the children agree to think of (individually brainstorm) as many questions and/or problems related to weights and measures as they can. The class tackles one or more of the questions or problems each day. The first question drawn from the question box reads: "I've heard people say that 'a pint's a pound the world around.' Is this statement true?" The class discusses the meaning of the question. One group of children agree to fill a pint container with several different liquids and then weigh them. Bill

Janis, a student, makes this comment: "Pints and quarts and things like that are measures of volume. So what the question about the pint and pound is, is whether or not a certain volume always has the same weight." The class generally agrees with Bill's explanation. Cynthia, another student, reminds the class that they have already learned that air pressure and gravity affect the weight of an object. So they know right away that a pint of the same liquid would not weigh the same on Mount Everest and in Death Valley. "A pint would weigh nothing in outer space," Vickie chimes in. "My father says a ton of feathers weighs the same as a ton of iron," Jimmy Preston adds.

Miss Ellis' class has been launched on a problem-solving adventure of general class interest. Many creative solutions *may arrive* from the experience if Miss Ellis can help to maintain a free-wheeling, open-minded intellectual atmosphere in her classroom. No suggestion, even though it might seem ridiculous, is cast aside without serious consideration.

Miss Ellis' class is learning how to explore many variables of a problem dealing with weights and measures. The exploration of variables will help children to realize that any problem has a galaxy of ramifications, which the creative thinker fastidiously examines.

Energy Units—An Open-ended Area of Measurement

An area of measurement that is becoming increasingly important is that of measuring energy. Energy measurement units such as horsepower and manpower have been used for many years, but man's conquest of outer space requires a completely new set of units to measure generated energy. Reference reading regarding the Mercury, Gemini, and Apollo space flights can help to supply students with the needed background information for discussing the types of generated energy that need to be measured. An astronaut floating in a condition of weightlessness propels himself about by a type of jet gun that triggers small bursts of energy. What type of energy units are called for to describe this form of propulsion? As a result of reference reading relative to man's space flights, have the class tell what other types of energy units have been created and named.

A Quart Does Not Always Resemble a Quart!

Weights and measures take on some strange shapes as they are projected into modern packaging techniques. A visit with a group of students to any supermarket can help to dramatize this point. Most children have a mental image of a quart as being the size and shape of a quart milk bottle. Yet a quart container can be made in a limitless number of shapes, some of which make the quart container appear much larger than a quart. For example, false bottoms and pinching the middle of the bottle can make the quart appear larger. (See the three quart containers shown in Figure 8–12.)

PINCHED-IN
SIDES

SCOOPED-IN
BOTTOM

WHEN FILLED TO CAPACITY, ALL THREE CONTAINERS SHOWN ABOVE HOLD EXACTLY ONE QUART OF LIQUID. DO THEY ALL APPEAR TO BE THE SAME SIZE?

FIGURE 8–12. *Varying shapes of the quart*

Food packagers are required by law to state on any box, bottle, or package the weight or measurement of the food contained within. Likewise, the product must fill the package. But there are many interpretations as to what constitutes "filling the package." The Food and Drug Administration remains vigilant against misleading labeling and packaging practices, yet many consumers are deceived about the size of a package. It is difficult to determine by eye the amount of food contained in a box, bottle, or package. Figure 8–13 shows two boxes of cereal food. On a grocer's shelf the box of Whamo might appear to be much larger than the box of Zanies because the box of Whamos has greater height. But actually the box of Whamo is the smaller container of the two. Children should be made aware of the mechanics of packaging. This type of learning is, to say the least, practical.

FIGURE 8–13. *Which is larger, the Zanies or the Whamo?*

Even though the box of Zanies is larger than the box of Whamo, many other factors can affect the monetary value of either box of cereal. Although there may be less cereal (in terms of bulk weight) in the box of Whamo, there may be greater nutritional value in the cereal itself. This can usually be determined by the list of ingredients given on each box of cereal. Often the mineral contents of the food are listed in milligrams, a measure the class may decide to investigate.

Sometimes a class elects to make a collection of food containers such as boxes, cartons, bottles, packages, etc., that might be considered misleading in terms of the quantity (weight) of food they contain. This activity can be an exciting, detective-like pursuit out of which children may develop greater sensitivity to the mechanics of packaging.

Some scientists and mathematicians would have our nation drop the standard weights and measures we use in favor of the metric system. A comparison of the advantages and disadvantages of the two systems is another area in which much student interest can easily be generated.

For students who develop intense interest in weights and meas-ures, the teacher should suggest other aspects of weights and meas-ures which can be explored. Some students may want to investigate a few of the newer mediums of measurement. To mention only a few: sound, light rays, and electricity are being used to measure vari-ous elements of our environment. Perhaps, beginning with a few unusual measurement terms, students may "discover" an entirely new avenue of measurement: decibels, foot-candles, gms, ohms, btu's.

Rekindling Student Interest in a Unit

If student interest lags a bit during your weights and measurements unit, it may be helpful to introduce weights and measures as they apply to hunting, fishing, and trapping laws. Some girls and boys will become intensely interested in the subject if, for example, fishing laws are discussed.

Creating Your Own System of Weights and Measures

After some exposure to and experience with existing systems of weights and measures, children should be called upon to create new systems of weights and measures. In addition, they should have the opportunity to actually use their new systems of weights and meas-ures in some problem-solving situations. Since all weights and meas-ures are ideas (the products of man's mind), new ideas or modifica-tions of existing ones are in order.

* * *

Miss Ellis' class decides to develop some new systems of weights and measures as homework. Nick Romona is the first student to re-port back to the class the results of his efforts. Nick elected to create a new system of linear measures. Some other students chose to work on measures of area and volume. Nick shows his basic linear unit on a small piece of paper; he calls it a "glop." He explains that the length of the glop is the width of one of his eyes from corner to corner. Because this is true he carries the basic length of the glop with him. He can quickly obtain its length by placing a finger at each corner of his eye. Nick introduces his other units: a grinch (equal to 10 glops) and a gelder (equal to 5 grinches or 50 glops). Nick pro-duces a stick that is 1 grinch in length; it is marked off like a ruler into 10 glops. Nick explains that since his linear measures involve numerals ending in either 5 or 0, they are easier to compute with than the 12-inch foot or the 36-inch yard used in conventional linear measure. A lively discussion follows Nick's introduction of his new linear measures.

Creating New Measures of Time

One topic that can be open-ended and intriguing for students to investigate is time. It is certainly one dimension of life which children find difficult to understand. Further, it is a dimension of life that can be perceived as having mathematical characteristics.

The space age has brought about the necessity to examine the element of time and man's relationship to time in many new frames of reference. As an example, the tremendous speed of jet airliners makes it possible to leave London, England, fly the Atlantic Ocean to New York City, and arrive at a time *earlier* than the departure time in London. It is like saying we arrived in New York before we left London! The dimension of time projected into problems of outer-space travel leaves many questions as yet unanswered by our most capable scientists and mathematicians.

Young children, in order to apply their own creative thinking toward divisions of time, must first develop some understandings about the nature of time as mankind presently perceives it. Children and adults do not create in a vacuum. Using reference books, children can be motivated to find out how and why we presently measure time on earth. They are apt to discover the relationships between the earth's rotation and revolution and our standard units of measuring time. Students may see the relationship between the phases of the moon and the so-called lunar month. The seven-day week and the twelve-month year can be perceived as mod 7 and mod 12 number systems. This leads to the question: Is time actually circular in configuration, or is the existence of modular methods of delineating time strictly man's perception of time? If man travels into space far enough from the earth to lose its revolution and rotation as frames of reference, how else could he measure time? The more able students in the upper levels of the elementary school are quite capable of coping with this type of problem provided they have done some reference reading relative to space travel and astronomy.

Younger students may find it of personal significance to try to plan divisions of time other than the standard minute, hour, day, week, month, and year. Ignoring the lunar phases and other natural phenomena (such as the rotation and revolution of the earth), they can attempt to create divisions of time completely different from the conventional ones. A nine-year-old boy named Scott Preston suggested a plan to organize time into standard months. That is, each month would have exactly 32 days and would contain four 8-day weeks. Therefore, each month would begin with the same day (Sunday), and each date, such as the 12th day of the month, would always fall on the same day of the week (Wednesday in the case of the 12th).

A diagram of Scott's reorganized "month" appears in Figure 8–14.

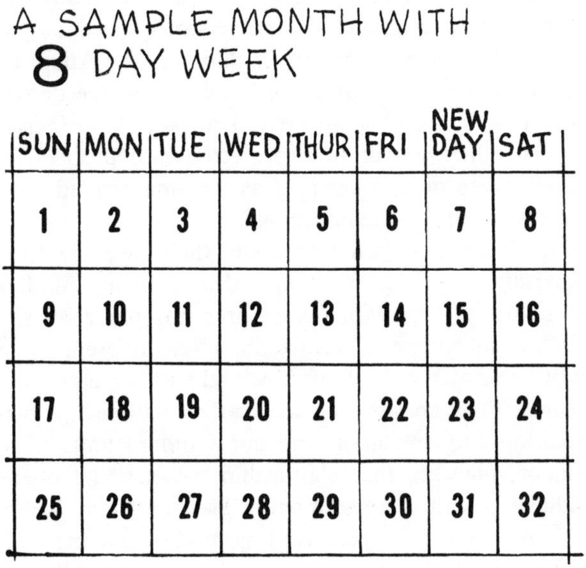

A SAMPLE MONTH WITH 8 DAY WEEK

SUN	MON	TUE	WED	THUR	FRI	NEW DAY	SAT
1	2	3	4	5	6	7	8
9	10	11	12	13	14	15	16
17	18	19	20	21	22	23	24
25	26	27	28	29	30	31	32

FIGURE 8–14. *Scott Preston's standardized month*

Scott presented his 32-day-month, 8-day-week proposal to his classmates for discussion. Nancy asked if he would still hold to the idea of having 12 months a year. If so, 12 of his 32-day-months would make 384 days, which is more than the 365¼ days used by the earth to make one revolution around the sun. Was he throwing out the year as a measure of time? Scott explained that he would retain the solar year as a measure but his year would have only 11 months. This would leave 13 days unaccounted for in order to fill out the 365¼ days. Eleven months consisting of 32 days would encompass 352 days. The 13 days near the end of the year would be used as vacation days by everyone. Scott identified each of the vacation days as V-1, V-2, V-3, V-4 . . . V-13. Leap year would have V-14.

The questions and discussion came in torrents. Much of it hinged upon what effects Scott's new calendar might have on everyday living. The class became intensely committed to investigating and experimenting with *other* plans for measuring and identifying the time dimension.

Perhaps it would be best to throw out the month as a unit of time and devise some other unit of measure. And what about the time belts that are patterned around the world? Couldn't a better system than the belt idea be devised? Try having your students experiment with designing new concepts and measurements of time.

Springboards for Creativity in Mathematics

The body travels more easily than the mind, and until we have limbered up our imagination we continue to think as though we had stayed home.

JOHN ERSKINE (1879–1951)

Algorisms in Color?

There are two dynamic interacting elements in an elementary-school classroom—the teacher and the group of children. Creativity can stem from one or the other of these elements, or both, during any particular teaching-learning experience. Not all creative teaching techniques that a teacher employs will promote creative thinking in children. Nor will all creative thinking from children encourage creative thinking on the part of the teacher, nor is it the result of the teaching act.

* * *

One day Miss Meredith puts the day's arithmetic algorisms (examples) on the greenboard in colored chalk. She makes remarks to the class: "Watch out for the red ones, they're really tricky." "The green ones [examples] were sent to me by the jolly green giant." Utilizing colored chalk with the arithmetic on the greenboard may be, for Miss Meredith, a creative use of teaching materials. There is a fluorescent chalk on the market which, when used with an ultraviolet light, will literally "glow." Algorisms written on a greenboard which "glow" can amaze children and add interest to a mathematics lesson. But while the children may derive a good deal of pleasure from the teacher's use of colored chalk, they may or may not be stimulated to engage in creative thinking. The entire matter depends upon the way in which Miss Meredith employs the colored chalk, plus a host of other human variables.

* Nine in Hindu-Arabic, about 1300 A.D.

158

Cross-number Puzzles

The cross-number puzzle is a variation of the cross-word puzzle using numbers in place of words. The cross-number puzzle can be used with any of the four basic processes of mathematics, as well as with other aspects of mathematics. After children understand the basic mechanics of how a cross-number puzzle works, they delight in creating original puzzles to challenge their classmates. Suggested puzzles are shown in Figures 9–1 and 9–2.

What objectives of teaching mathematics could the cross-number puzzle help to achieve? What variations of the cross-number puzzle can you think of which involve the intersection of numerals?

	Across		*Down*
B	$100 + 100 = ?$	A	$29 - 17 = ?$
C	Add 232 and 121	C	15
E	The sum of 50 and 50		$+15$
F	323		___
	118	D	12
	$+15$		$+19$
	___		___
		F	Twenty eight and twelve $=?$
		G	53 plus 53 $=?$

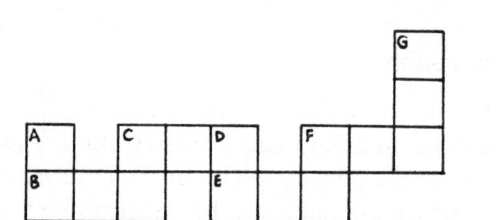

FIGURE 9–1. *Simplified cross-number puzzle for primary-level children*

Across	*Down*
b 126 (base 10) written in terms of a quinary number system	a The number of units in a score
	b $4^2 = ?$
d XXXVI = _____ in Hindu-Arabic numerals	c Number of inches in a linear foot
e The square of 5	

g The equivalent in base 10 of the ancient Egyptian number

∩∩∩   111
∩   111

h Number of ounces in a pound
i $25 + 2 \times 10 = ?$
k Number of years in a decade?
l $10^2 + 250 = ?$

d Number of days in one calendar year
f Five centuries plus a decade equal ? years.
j The number 43 in base 10 written in base 8
k The equivalent of 12 (base 10) written in base 12
m Number of weeks in a year?

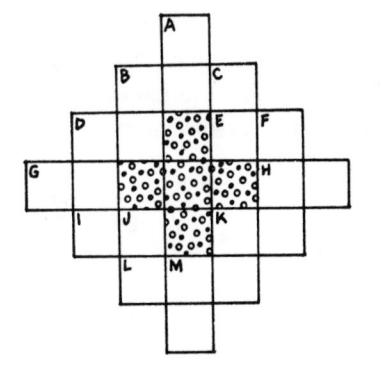

FIGURE 9–2. *Cross-number puzzle for upper-level elementary school*

Nutty Numeration

Young children are willing to examine open-mindedly ideas that most adults would reject as absurd and worthless. As a result, the teacher of mathematics in the primary grades of the elementary school is in an enviable position. He can focus the children's high tolerance level for fantasy into some types of mathematics activities. For example, the teacher and his students can do some fanciful counting by assigning new names each time a base is reached in counting. The conventional name assigned to reaching base once is "ten" (1 base and no ones: 10); reaching base twice is "twenty"; arriving at base the third time is called "thirty." But supposing the teacher and his students assign animal names to each base and its powers. They discuss the problem, and finally the teacher records the names agreed upon on the greenboard for all to use as a reference.

Reached base	Base 10 We write it like this:	We call it:	Today we will call it:
1 time	10	ten	monkey
2 times	20	twenty	hippopotamus
3 times	30	thirty	elephant

Then, using the reference chart, the "counting" begins orally. It sounds like this: zero, one, two, three . . . nine, monkey (instead of the word "ten"), monkey one, monkey two, monkey three (13), monkey four . . . monkey nine, hippopotamus, hippopotamus one, hippopotamus two, hippopotamus three . . . hippopotamus nine, elephant, elephant one, elephant two, elephant three. . . . This activity might seem of little consequence to the reader, but it can help to reinforce in the minds of students the base 10 "idea" in our number system. Equally important, the activity can be great fun for young students and thereby assist in promoting positive attitudes toward mathematics.

There are limitless modifications of this activity which the teacher and his students can create. A first grade recorded each base by assigning names of classmates to them. The teacher helped the first-grade class to develop this chart:

This many	Base 10 We usually write it like this	We usually call it	Today we will call it
ten (one base)	10	ten	Patty
2 tens (two base)	20	twenty	Skipper
3 tens (three base)	30	thirty	Billy

Then the first grade tested their new plan for "fun counting." This is what the counting sounded like: zero, one, two, three, four, five . . . nine, Patty, Patty one, Patty two (12), Patty three . . . Patty nine, Skipper, Skipper one, Skipper two, Skipper three . . . Skipper nine, Billy, Billy one, Billy two, Billy three . . . and so on. Perhaps the reader will be able to hitchhike some modifications of "fun counting" to employ with children. How could this "fun counting" idea be projected into another base system? What might "fun counting" sound like in base 5?

Create New Mathematics Symbolization

Mathematics is literally loaded with standardized symbols. They indicate the relationships among numbers and/or the type of process that is to be performed on the numbers. Some of the most common symbols are: $=, \times, +, -, \div, \sqrt{}$.

Mathematical symbols have not always been the same; for example, see Figure 9–7 for the evolution of the decimal point. New symbols are being created as the need arises. A symbol, however, has value only if you know what it means, which is one reason for the standardization of symbols. Mathematics would be extremely difficult if the meanings of its symbols were constantly changing.

Children can be stimulated to create original symbols and an accompanying meaning for each one. After doing this, a group of students may want to use the new symbols in mathematical computation. It can be an exciting experience for a student to have his classmates actually use the new mathematical symbol he has created. A ten-year-old girl developed this symbol: $\square$. She explained that her new symbol means you add five times the first number to the second number. Therefore, 6 $\square$ 5 = 35, and 10 $\square$ 14 = 64.

To oil up your own "symbol-creating ability," create a symbol that means *multiply the two numbers and divide by 3.*

Creating original mathematical symbols and their meanings can be interest-provoking for children. This is especially true when the newly created symbols are actually put to use in their daily classroom mathematics.

Creative Filing with Mathematics

Many children have seen cards used in data processing that have holes punched in them. Some students will find it an intriguing and challenging experience to design an original filing system utilizing mathematics with punch cards. The information for the filing system can pertain to fellow-students. Three-by-five or five-by-eight index cards will serve nicely as punch cards. If need be, the cards can be cut from oak tag, poster board, or heavy paper.

The easiest number system to employ in filing punch cards is a binary number system. (If you are not familiar with the mechanics of a binary system, turn to Chapter 11.) Three sixth-grade classes working together developed a series of personal data items that were printed on five-by-eight cards with the school's liquid duplicating machine. Then each student was requested to fill out one of the cards, supplying personal data where requested. A committee punched holes in all of the cards in a predetermined pattern so that the holes on all of the cards were lined up in the same manner. A sample card is shown in Figure 9–3, in reduced size, after the holes had been punched in it.

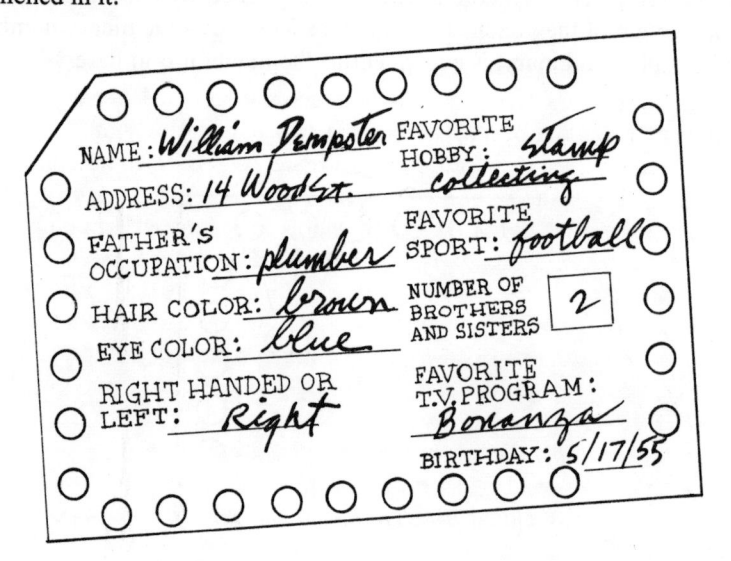

FIGURE 9–3. *Sample personal data card*

In the three sixth-grade classes there are ninety-seven students. Consequently, ninety-seven different five-by-eight cards were assembled into one large pack of cards. This is a large quantity from which to get information; for example, to find the names of all of the students whose favorite hobby is stamp collecting, one would have to sort through ninety-seven cards. This is a formidable task.

One way to make any specific information on the cards available at once is to employ some type of mathematical code system for filing the information. A limitless number of mathematical patterns can be employed to do this. Mr. Keith Preston, one of the sixth-grade teachers, suggested to the three classes that a binary number system be used as a beginning experience with mathematical filing. The students discussed Mr. Preston's suggestion and agreed that the simplicity of a binary number system would be best for experimenting with mathematical filing and sorting. The term *sorting* was added to the description of the task when several children expressed the view that the task they wanted to accomplish involved not only filing information but rapidly sorting it.

Since a binary number system uses only two symbols (1 and 0, for example), the sixth-graders, with Mr. Preston's guidance, decided that each punched hole along the edges of the cards would stand for 0. The numeral 1 would be expressed by cutting away the top portion of the punched hole. Figure 9–8 shows the binary number 110, which, in binary, is equivalent to the numeral 6 in base 10.

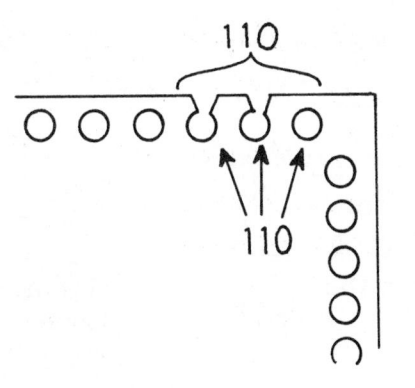

FIGURE 9–4. *The binary number 110*

Then Mr. Preston and the students assigned a binary number to each one of the characteristics that were found on any of the ninety-seven cards. This is a time-consuming procedure. However, the process of assigning a separate number to each bit of information is the heart of the mathematical system of filing. And, once the students understand the basic principle involved here, they can go on and create variations on the basic idea.

The basic principle of assigning binary numbers to specific information is not complicated. In this instance, the students, using binary notation, worked out the following notation for hair color: brown = 1; black = 10; blonde = 11; red = 100; auburn = 101;

light brown = 111. Thus it was possible to record any one of the six different hair colors by use of only three of the holes punched in the card. The students decided which three holes of every punch card would be used to record hair color.

Two holes were designed to depict handedness: 1 = right-handed; 10 = left-handed; 11 = ambidextrous. One punch hole was assigned to record sex: 0 = male; 1 = female. A specific binary number was assigned for each bit of information they wanted filed mathematically.

To illustrate very simply how the mathematical filing and sorting works, let us use the three categories of information that have already been described: hair color, handedness, and sex. Figure 9-5 shows William Dempster's card "punched" to indicate that he is a brown-haired boy who is right-handed. See how the punched holes

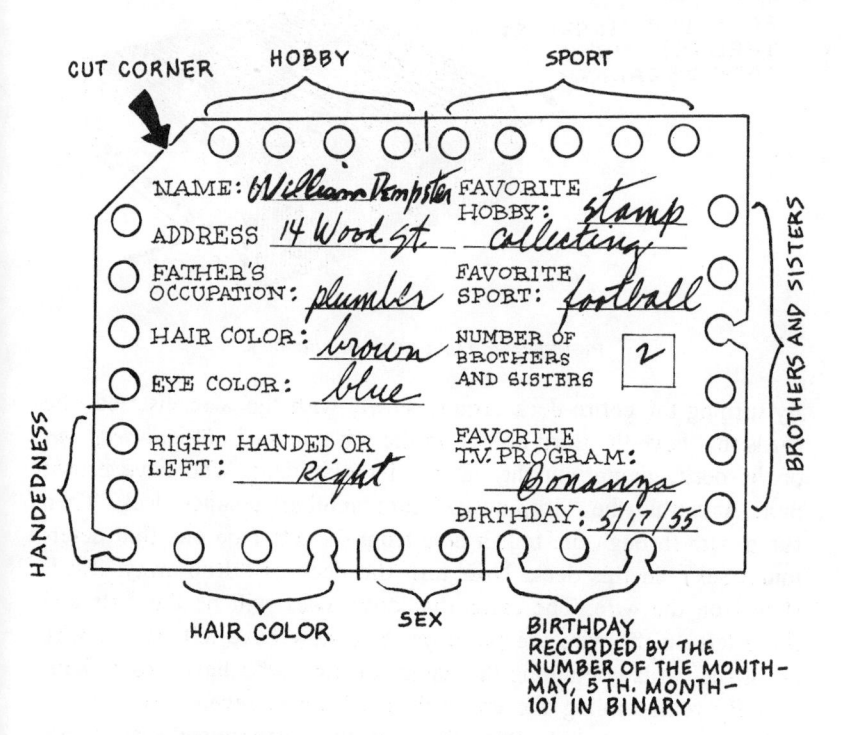

EACH CATEGORY OF INFORMATION HAS ITS OWN SET OF HOLES

FIGURE 9–5. *Personal data card, punched*

are either left intact or cut away to indicate William's hair color, handedness, and sex.

After they have been punched and cut in accordance with the binary code established by Mr. Preston and his students, the ninety-seven cards can be sorted almost instantaneously with some straight pieces of stiff wire. Suppose someone wanted to know the names of all of the boys among the ninety-seven students who are right-handed and have brown hair. First, put all of the cards into one deck so that the cut corners are in line, as shown in Figure 9–6. When the cut corners are in line, all the cards are right side up. A stiff wire is inserted in the third hole from the left, the one that indicates brown hair. Be certain that the wire goes through the entire deck of cards.

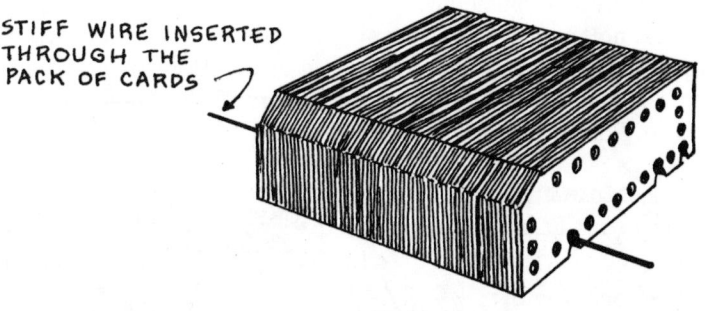

FIGURE 9–6. *Data cards in one deck*

By turning the entire deck around slowly with the wire inserted, the cards that have the third hole from the left punched out *will drop out* of the deck, giving you the names of the students who have brown hair. Assemble the "drop-aways" into another, smaller deck. Then run a wire through the fourth hole from the left (the one that determines sex), in this deck. Now turn the deck of "drop-away" cards slowly on the wire. The cards that drop away will be the girls and those left on the wire are the boys. You now have left on the wire all of the cards containing the names of boys who have brown hair.

By reassembling the entire deck of ninety-seven cards in any order, wires can be run through the deck to separate the cards according to any of the categories that are coded by the punched holes along the sides of the cards.

The filing and sorting experience through which Mr. Preston

guided the three sixth-grade classes was designed as an orientation to the general principles involved in simple punch-card operation using a mathematical code. The orientation experience as such offered little if any open-endedness into which the students could interject creative responses. The function of the experience with the cards is to demonstrate an established method of mathematical sorting or filing from which the children can hitchhike variations and create better systems for mathematical coding.

Teaching the History of Our Number System in the Elementary School

The evolution of numerals, weights, measures, and systems of mathematical notation can be fascinating to children when presented meaningfully. Children are usually amazed at the vast number of changes that have occurred throughout the history of the Hindu-Arabic system of mathematical notation. The ten seemingly uncomplicated numerals (0–9) which form the basic notation of our number system owe their existence to thousands of years of mathematical evolution. Planning mathematical learning experiences for children relative to the evolution of numbers offers an ideal opportunity for the classroom teacher to correlate social studies with mathematics.

Mathematics Undergoing Constant Change

Contrary to the image many teachers give it, mathematics is not a static discipline. It is composed of ideas, most of which have gone through an evolutionary cycle. A study of the history of mathematics can help children to trace portions of the evolution. In doing so the children may realize that the systems of notation, and all of the basic elements of mathematics, are ever changing as new interpretations are applied and as the needs of society change. The emergence of nuclear power and our space program, for instance, have called for new mathematics. In sum, mathematics is a reflection and reporting of man's quantitative thinking.

If the teacher will help children to "break off small pieces" of mathematics and interpret them in as many ways as possible, they may see some of the infinite beauty that lies within. (Comparably, the student of science examines the wing of a fly under a microscope and is amazed by its intricate and functional construction.) Even such a seemingly mundane symbol as the decimal point has an evolutionary background reflecting variations made by different mathematicians. Figure 9–7 shows five methods of expressing the decimal idea other than the one used today. The object of the decimal point is simply to express fractions that employ a power of ten as the denominator. Perhaps your students will want to discuss other ideas for expressing decimal fractions.

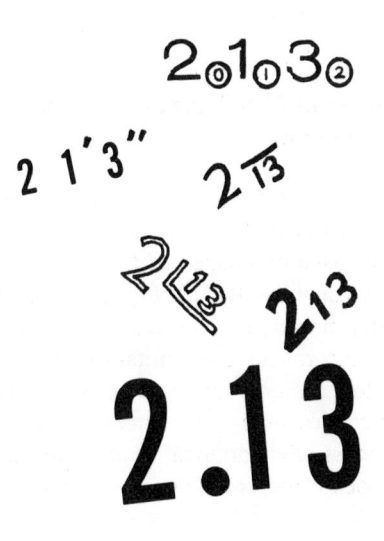

FIGURE 9–7. *Evolution of the decimal point*

Decimal fractions can be made exciting and challenging for children. Decimals need not be "dismals," as one student called them.

Literally any implement used in daily living contains certain fundamental elements which have been retained throughout its evolution. Likewise, in studying the evolution of number systems as they occur in the history of man, children can be led to discover the basic elements that are common to all number systems.

Design and Mathematics

Number sentences and equations can be constructed to represent many graphic designs. This type of activity can be most helpful in readying children for working with more complex mathematical equations. Even more, we can promote creative thinking in children by having them construct original designs and then compose mathematical notation to represent the designs. As an introduction, the teacher may want to show his students designs on sample pieces of drapery and clothing material, rugs, wall paper, or even the end papers of children's books. Figure 9–8 shows a section of wallpaper border, whose design is represented by an equation written beneath it. The equation, as explained by the child who constructed it, means: one spiral (1 sp) plus three circles (3 c) plus one spiral (1 sp) plus three circles (3 c) plus one flower (1 f) equals the design unit (d.u.). The design unit is repetitive. The child also has written the equation in simplified form.

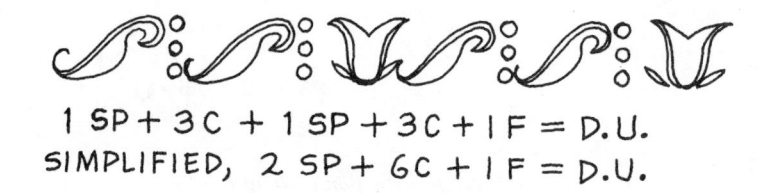

$$1\ SP + 3C + 1\ SP + 3C + 1\ F = D.U.$$
$$SIMPLIFIED,\ 2\ SP + 6C + 1\ F = D.U.$$

FIGURE 9–8. *Design with equation*

The composition of a repetitive design can be worked out by children in the primary grades with the aid of the teacher and a flannel board. The children can be encouraged to cut out of heavy paper objects which they would like to incorporate in a design. The teacher may want to supply the components of the design the first time the class engages in this activity. Bits of sandpaper pasted on the back of the paper objects will allow them to cling to the flannel board. Colored circles, squares, rectangles, even free-form shapes may be employed.

Figure 9–9 depicts a design placed on a flannel board by several first graders. The class discussed how they might write a "sentence" using symbols to represent their design. One number sentence the class constructed is as follows: 3 balls + 2 blocks + 3 balls + 2 blocks + 1 toy jet plane = 1 design. Simplified, 6 balls + 4 blocks + 1 toy jet plane = 1 design.

Part of a design from an oriental rug is shown in Figure 9–10.

Letters have been assigned to the various parts of the design to identify them. Notice the number sentence that describes the design, and its simplification. Create a design of your own and describe it with a number sentence.

FIGURE 9–9. *First-graders' flannel-board design*

$$X + 2Y + Z + 2Y + X = \text{DESIGN}$$
$$\text{SIMPLIFIED: DESIGN} = 2X + 4Y + 1Z$$

FIGURE 9–10. *Oriental rug pattern with equation*

Sets to Grow on

Lead-up activities can serve as gradual intellectual steps toward the complex algebraic ideas that will be presented to children at a later time. An informal introduction to the use of signs and symbols in notating sets can be presented to children by using a chart or individual cards similar to those shown in Figures 9–11(a) and (b).

LARGE TEDDY BEAR   SMALL TEDDY BEAR   LARGE BALL   SMALL BALL

TWO CONCRETE OBJECTS USED IN THE SETS. EACH OBJECT COMES IN TWO SIZES--LARGE AND SMALL.

FIGURE 9–11(a). *Simplified sets chart employing concrete objects*

The chart and cards employ two objects: a teddy bear and a ball. Most children at the primary levels of the elementary school are capable of working with this type of simple symbolization. The capital letter T is used to symbolize *teddy bear* and a capital B for *ball*. The capital letter L is employed to symbolize *large,* and a capital S is used to represent *small.* The foregoing correspondence of symbols and words is also shown in the key to Figure 9–11(b). Examine square number 1 of the simplified sets chart. The set shown in square number 1 on the chart can be symbolized as (L T + S B).

CARD #1

CARD #2

CARD #3

CARD #4

KEY TO SYMBOLS:

S = small   T = teddy bear
L = large   B = bear

USING THE SYMBOLS SUGGESTED BY THE KEY, CARD 1 CAN BE DESCRIBED AS (ST + LT), CARD 2 AS (LB + ST), CARD 3 (SB + LB) AND CARD 4 AS (SB + SB).

FIGURE 9–11(b). *Single set cards constructed by teacher and/or students*

The children should be stimulated to make comparisons among the various squares on the chart. (Which sets contain similar objects? What are the differences between the specific set cards?) They also should be encouraged to create some set cards and charts of their own employing other objects. Perhaps the children will want to develop sets with three or more objects to further complicate the symbolization for each set. Figure 9–12 shows two set cards suggested by a child in the primary level. Since a duck appears on both cards, the teacher can lead the learners to observe that the two sets have one common overlapping element. From this example, the idea of intersection of sets could be developed using other set cards to reinforce the understanding.

FIGURE 9–12. *Set cards: objects drawn on two pieces of cardboard*

In constructing original set cards, children could cut pictures of objects from magazines and paste them on cards, or draw objects with art materials. As well as making the set cards and charts, the children, in concert with the teacher, can develop original symbolization to accompany the charts. Most six-year-olds will find the set cards and symbols well within the scope of their mental abilities.

The chart and cards (including the key) shown in Figure 9–13 represent a more sophisticated and complex mental challenge. The teddy bear and ball were objects easily identifiable to children; for most of them the two have been a part of their childhood environment. The objects utilized in Figure 9–13 are more abstract in character. A rectangle and a cone constitute the visual objects. In addition, another factor has been incorporated which complicates the symbolization a bit more. This is *texture,* represented by the letters D (dotted) and G (grooved). Therefore, in putting together a set of symbols that describe the set cards or sets chart it will be necessary to assign symbols to represent the texture factor. Figure 9–13 needs

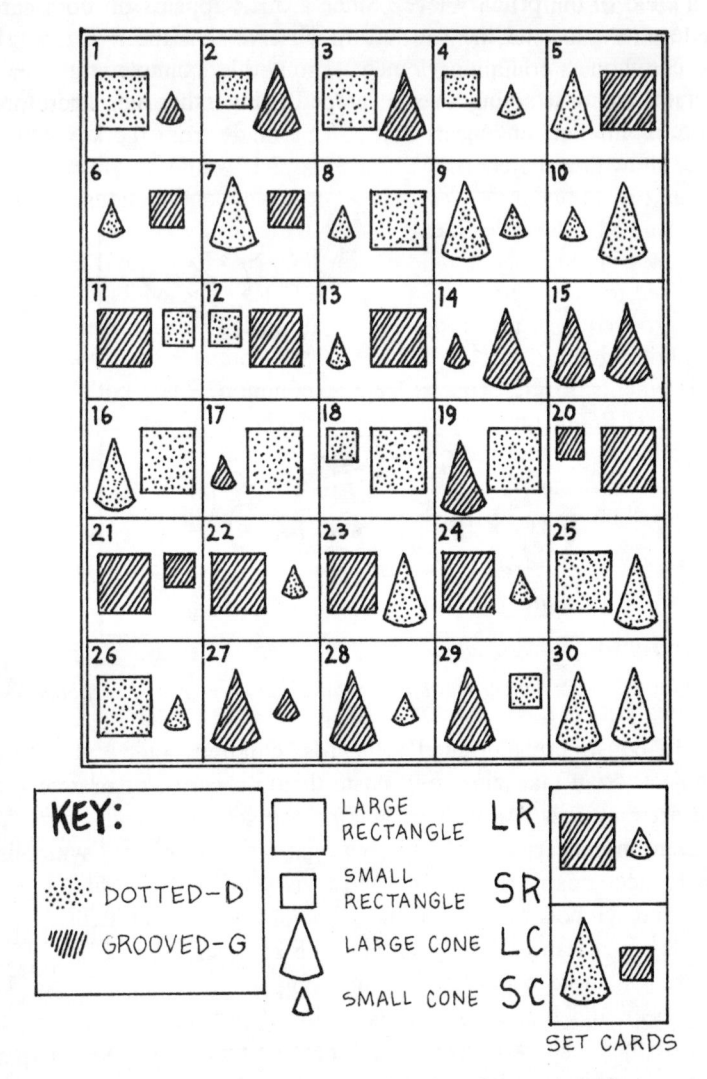

FIGURE 9–13. *Sets chart containing thirty set cards*

six symbols to describe all of the elements present in the key. Let us assign the following symbols to represent the elements for purposes of explanation: L = Large; S = Small; C = Cone; R = Rectangle; G = Grooved; and D = Dotted. With these six symbols it is possible to describe fully each set of two objects represented on either the sets chart or the set cards.

There are only two set cards shown in Figure 9–13. It is assumed that the teacher, with the children, would construct a quantity of set cards, each containing a variation. The sets chart can be used as a guide to constructing a set of cards, if this is desired. There are other combinations of objects that can be made from the key which are not shown on the chart. What are they? It would be valuable for children to "brainstorm" *all* of the possible combinations for set cards using only the six elements shown in the key.

Now examine sets 17 and 19 on the sets chart. Set 17 can be symbolized in this manner: (S G C + L D R). The symbols indicate "small grooved cone plus large dotted rectangle." Set number 19 can be symbolized as (L G C + L D R). Now compare set 17 with 19. What elements do the two sets have in common? They both contain G C + L D R. As a teacher, you can guide children in comparing the sets. Children will find it a mental challenge and great fun. To inject more open-endedness into this activity, encourage the students to "dream up" more sets charts and/or set cards of their own.

Creativity and Magic Squares

Since creativity is a type of human "magic," it is understandable that mathematical magic squares can become vehicles for promoting creativity in children. There is nothing magic about magic squares, yet they can be used by the teacher and students as springboards for creativity with numbers. For the reader who is not familiar with magic squares, two such squares are illustrated in Figure 9–14.

Magic squares offer children the opportunity to discover number patterns and relationships. For example, in square number 1 the sum of the diagonal corners is 10. Each vertical row of the square totals 15; and the numbers in each horizontal row yield a sum of 15. The three numbers that are diagonal (8, 5, 2) and (4, 5, 6) also total 15. Magic square number 2 is a very famous one. It can be found in a painting titled "Melancolia" by Albrecht Dürer, which dates back to 1514.

Elementary school children can create their own magic squares. The teacher who would promote discovery and creativity in pupils will encourage them to experiment in an attempt to discover a pattern or formula for constructing a magic square. For the information of the teacher, a magic square of *any* size (*number of squares*) can be constructed as long as it contains an *odd* number of columns and rows.

FIGURE 9–14. *The magic squares*

What types of mathematical creativity can grow out of magic squares? The teacher can challenge her students to produce "magic diamonds," "magic pentagons," "magic snakes," or *any* of an unlimited number of *interlocking* number series or patterns.

Figure 9–15 shows two original number constructions created by a third-grade child. These constructions are limitless in terms of possible variations and can present a truly open-ended challenge.

Mosaics and Mathematics

Mosaics can be another springboard to creativity and the ability to write number sentences. Figure 9–16 contains two mosaics that can serve as examples for the teacher.

Although mosaics can be made in an untold number of shapes and sizes, space restrictions have limited the authors to only two square mosaics. The involvement of brilliant color in mosaics appeals

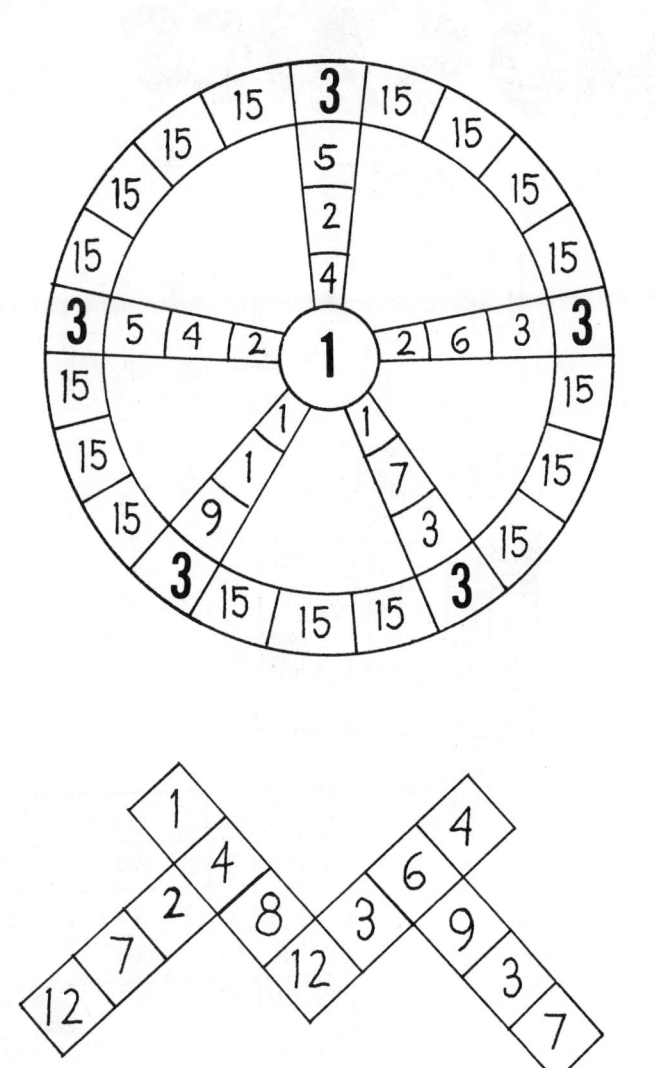

FIGURE 9–15. *A fifteen wheel and a twenty-five pattern*

to young students. After using one or two mosaics to illustrate some of their inherent basic mathematics, the teacher should challenge students to design their own mosaics and to describe mathematical relationships within them.

If the reader has had little experience in correlating mosaics and

MOSAICS

AND

MATH!

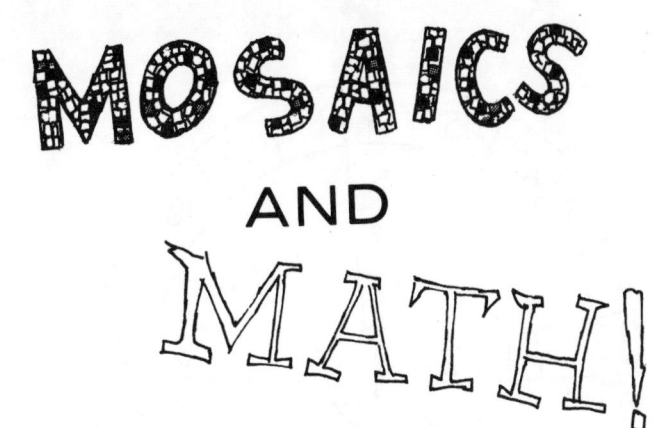

#1

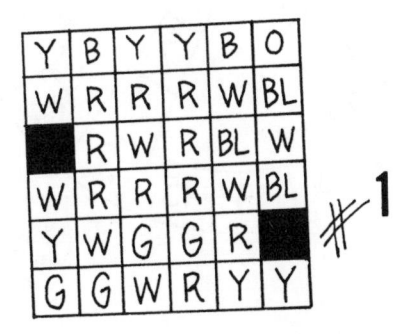

#2

FIGURE 9–16. *Examples of mosaics*

mathematics, the following explanation may be of assistance. It is helpful to standardize some symbols with your students in order to facilitate good communication. Let us use single lower-case letters as abbreviations for the various colors: b = brown; y = yellow; o = orange; bl = blue; w = white; r = red; g = green. A lower case *s* will mean square or squares. Therefore, the symbols l y s mean one yellow square. Once the teacher and students have agreed upon a system of standard notation, they are ready to go to work on the mosaics. Below the reader will find the first horizontal row of mosaic number one of Figure 9–16 reproduced.

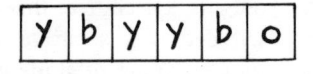

$$1\,y\,s + 1\,b\,s + 2\,y\,s + 1\,b\,s + 1\,o\,s = 6\,s \text{ (six squares =}$$
$$\text{total number in the row)}$$

This type of activity can be an enrichment experience for children relative to the construction of equations. The equation above can be simplified to:

$$(1 + 2)\,y\,s + (1 + 1)\,b\,s + 1\,o\,s = 6\,s$$

It is also interesting to ask children to point out common elements in two horizontal rows. If we consider the first and second rows of mosaic number two as shown below, we find that the two white squares are the only colored squares that *each* of the two rows has in common. Each horizontal or vertical row can be considered a set. Since rows one and two of mosaic two are similar in that each

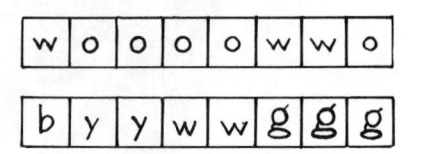

contains two white squares, we can show them to *intersect* at that point. The intersection could be diagrammed as shown below:

Row 1 contains   *Row 2 contains*

1 w s + 4 o s + 1 o s + 2 w s + 1 b s + 2 y s + 3 g s

Encourage your students to design mosaics in any shape and to represent the mosaics with mathematical equations.

The Institute of Personality Assessment and Research of the University of California has experimented with mosaics. Their findings indicate that highly creative people prefer mosaics that are not obviously patterned or structured. You may be able to observe this preference in your own students. Of course, this is only one piece of evidence; it cannot by itself definitely separate highly creative individuals from a heterogeneous grouping of students. But a highly creative person's preference for unpatterned mosaics can be helpful to the intelligent teacher. As an example, the highly creative individual would tend to prefer mosaic number three to mosaic number four in Figure 9–17.

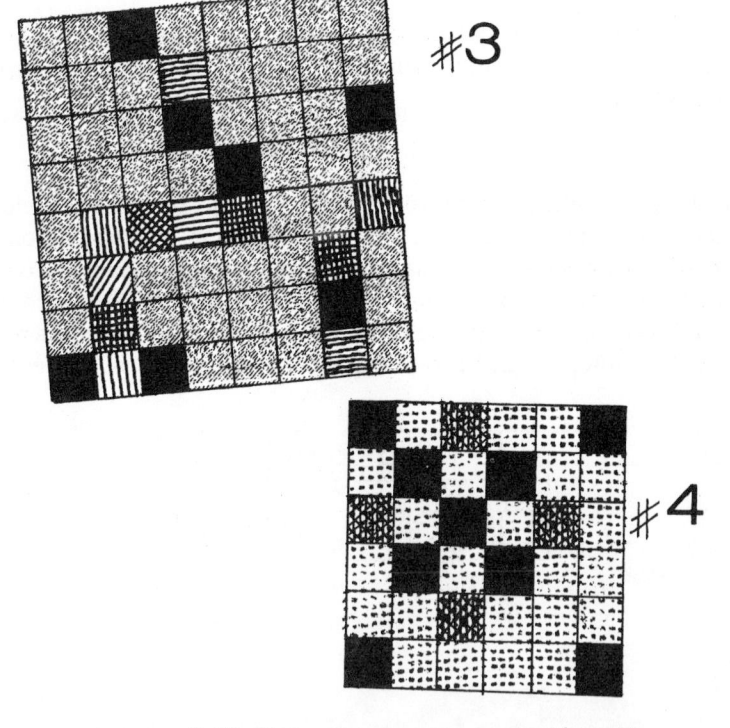

FIGURE 9–17. *Unstructured versus structured mosaic*

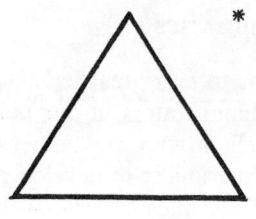
Evaluation and Creative Mathematics

> *. . . If a man does not keep pace with his companions, perhaps it is because he hears a different drummer. Let him step to the music which he hears, however measured or far away.*
>
> HENRY DAVID THOREAU, *Walden*

How Can We Evaluate?

Creative teaching of mathematics is the result of teacher planning. It is deliberate, not accidental. It is the result of planning in terms of clearly defined objectives, selecting methods to meet the objectives, and identifying evaluation techniques to appraise pupil progress and help plan future objectives. The most reliable and defensible evaluation of a mathematics lesson is in relation to the objectives prescribed in advance. This is the frame of reference against which the occurrences within the lesson *can* be evaluated.

Toward a More Clinical Analysis of Creative Teaching

To attempt to analyze creative teaching in a clinical manner is in many respects analogous to attempting to hold a moonbeam in your hand. Creative teaching, by many experts' definitions, is so varied, individualized, and inconsistent that it would seem to defy any kind of objective analysis. Yet what is highly creative teaching but a modification and/or variation of the teaching act? If we can determine the behavioristic norms of the teaching act as such, why can we not also determine those behaviors that are inherent in highly creative teaching?

In observing some teachers of mathematics, one might detect a great many behaviors that are apart from the behavioristic norms of the teaching act; others would give evidence of fewer variations. For this reason, creative teaching is a relative commodity. It is inaccurate to conceptualize two distinct classifications of teachers—creative and

* Greek symbol for ten.

noncreative. There are some creative aspects to *every* teacher's classroom performance. But supervisors and administrators in our public schools generally agree that there are teachers who are immensely different from their colleagues in terms of their ability to develop new ideas, construct original teaching aids, and see unusual relationships among subject-matter areas. It is this group of teachers, whom their peers and supervisors quickly identify as "creative," that the profession needs to examine more clinically.

We have in the past been satisfied with tossing around very loosely the phrase "creative teacher." It would be extremely helpful in terms of promoting excellence in teaching to analyze those aspects of the highly creative teacher's performance which will lend themselves to objective observation and measurement. If this can be accomplished, the outcome might be used to help other teachers. Do highly creative teachers perform their teaching act intuitively, or can they explain their thought processes? Do highly creative teachers of mathematics differ in any significant ways from highly creative teachers in general? These and many other important questions relative to the highly creative teacher remain unanswered by research.

Identification and Evaluation of Creative Teaching Need Not Be Crude

Clinical analysis of creative teaching is in its infancy. There are, however, two accepted bases from which evaluation can emanate.

1. *Highly creative teaching is performed by creative personalities.* There has been a great deal of research on the nature of the highly creative personality. The Thematic Apperception Test, Rorschach Test, and Minnesota Multiphasic Personality Inventory have assisted greatly in identifying the characteristics that differentiate highly creative persons from less creative ones. The work of Hargreaves (1927), Guilford and associates (1957), MacKinnon (1960), and Torrance (1959) (see Chapter 2 of this book), to name only a few, has given us a firm basis from which to draw evaluative criteria. To summarize: researchers have provided us with a great deal of information relative to the nature and behavior of the highly creative personality.

2. *No matter what definition of the teaching act one may choose to employ,* all *teachers engage in three common behaviors.* Regardless of their abilities and professional training, all teachers:

a. Establish objectives for their teaching (either consciously or unconsciously).
b. Plan activities, materials, and experiences to meet the objectives.
c. Devise techniques and instruments to measure, evaluate and report students' progress in terms of the objectives.

The manner in which a teacher engages in the three basic behaviors inherent in the teaching act can be observed, measured, and evaluated on a relative scale. Conventional and unconventional methods can be objectively identified. Therefore, creative approaches to at least these three aspects of the teaching act can be identified on a relative scale of frequency.

The Highly Creative Teacher Approaches the Teaching Act Uniquely

The highly creative teacher of mathematics undertakes the task of determining objectives for teaching in the following ways:

1. The objectives may be expressed in some type of unique written form.
2. The objectives may encompass a wider range of interrelationships between mathematics and other areas.

Remember that the highly creative individual frequently perceives relationships where average individuals do not. This was demonstrated recently while the authors were observing a student teacher present a mathematics lesson. The lesson was aimed at demonstrating the mathematical relationships that exist among intersections of sets, prime numbers, and least common denominators. The relationships the student teacher demonstrated were new not only to the students she was teaching but to most of the adults observing her lesson. This student teacher had determined the mathematical relationships while thinking through a method for teaching the determination of least common denominator (addition of fractions). Creative thinking was the means by which she had evolved the novel mathematical relationships.

A teacher at the intermediate level of the elementary school uses set concepts in discussing the relative position of his community in the world. For example, the United States is a member of the set of nations of the world. Then there is the set of the fifty states of the United States, of which the northeastern states constitute a subset.

And the states contain a set of counties, which in turn contain subsets of townships and cities. The application of the set concept to political divisions is an unusual but useful one for a teacher to make.

The highly creative teacher of mathematics also introduces variations commensurate with the objectives for the lesson in the selection, construction, and implementation of classroom activities and teaching aids. In like manner, the highly creative teacher makes innovations in the task of testing and evaluating student achievement in mathematics.

Two Human Elements in Evaluating the Teaching-Learning Process

There are two human elements that must be accounted for in evaluating the teaching-learning process: the behavior of the teacher(s) and the students (considered individually and as a group). As stated previously, a teacher may manifest much creative behavior in his teaching act, yet there is no guarantee that this will precipitate creative behavior in his students. Conversely, students sometimes engage in overt creative behavior while the classroom teacher gives much evidence of being a rigid, tightly structured personality.

A more ideal teaching-learning situation exists when the teacher and his students serve to stimulate creative thinking and overt creative behavior in each other. But we must be aware that creative teaching behaviors do not always beget creative responses from students.

The Two-Headed Evaluation Task

In order to evaluate a mathematics lesson, one must have data pertaining to the manner in which the teacher behaved during the mathematics lesson as well as performance data relative to the students who experienced the mathematics lesson. Therefore, evaluation of creative behavior in mathematics involves testing, measuring, and evaluating the behavior of both the students and the teacher. This is a monumental task, to say the least. The greatest obstacle at present is the fact that there is no clear-cut description of what constitutes highly creative teaching behavior in mathematics or, for that matter, of what constitutes highly creative student behavior in mathematics. Even with the Torrance list of characteristics, it is possible to produce deductively a list of only very general behaviors that constitute highly creative behavior in mathematics.

All behavior can be plotted on a relative scale. At present, the single most reliable criterion for plotting creative behavior seems to be the *uncommonness* of the behavior, which, unfortunately, disregards whether or not the behavior is of a constructive or destructive nature.

A response may be uncommon coming from one individual yet common in terms of the individual's peer group. Uncommon student performance in mathematics is best judged by a teacher who is familiar enough with the individual to recognize the uncommonness as such.

What Does a Creative Response Look Like?

In order to measure or assess a creative response, the teacher needs to have a mental picture of what a creative solution or response looks like (see Figure 10–1).

The circled P in the diagram composing Figure 10–1 represents a mathematical word problem to which a group of thirty children have been exposed. Each child is asked to make a list of as many

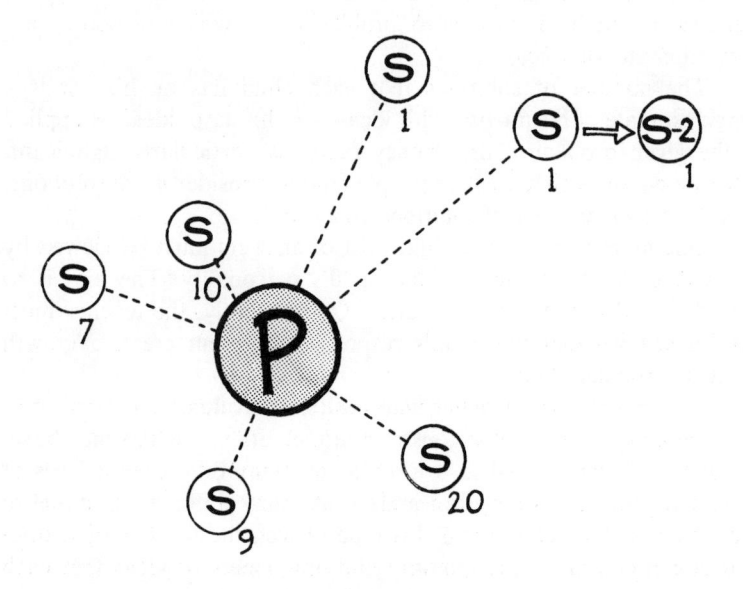

FIGURE 10–1. *A diagram of responses*

solutions as he can think of, and he is encouraged to construct as many answers as possible.

Assuming that all the children in the class have at least a general conception of what the problem asks for, their solutions can be compared and charted. We have not charted the *methods* the children used, but rather the *solutions* each child offered independently. The small circles containing the letter S represent the galaxy of solutions the class offered. Note that there is also a number included with each S; this represents the number of students in the class of thirty children who suggested this particular solution.

The thirty students suggested a total of forty-nine solutions in all. Of these only seven were different; the rest were repeats of the same solutions. There were three solutions that were offered only once, by one student. These three represent the most *uncommon* suggested by that particular class—not necessarily the most practical, but the most unique in terms of the group and therefore the *most creative*.

The solution labeled S-2 in Figure 10–1 is an example of "hitchhiking" a solution, meaning that the child evolved a solution as a result of being mentally triggered by another solution.

If, as a teacher, you work several years with the same *basic* mathematical material, you come to know what constitutes a typical response to mathematical word problems and which responses are very different—atypical.

The number of solutions that each child has on his list is a rough estimate of his *fluency* with ideas—in this case, ideas as applied to the given problem. This fluency factor is particularly significant, since we do know that creative people tend to consider *more* solutions, as well as a wider range of solutions, to a problem.

One more thing: Each child's list of answers must be viewed by the teacher in the context of the child's personality. The aim is to help the child become more creative. Consequently, the teacher must ask himself whether the child's responses represent creative growth for this particular child.

The mathematics teacher who desires to evaluate children's creative thinking abilities must construct test situations such as the above, in which children are asked to provide as many different methods of solving a problem as they can and/or as many different solutions to a problem as they can. From this type of test, the teacher of mathematics can determine the quantity and uniqueness of ideas that each child can provide within a specified time element. This type of mathematical testing is noticeably absent in some modern mathematics programs.

Objectives for Teaching and Evaluation of Students' Learning

One basic function of the teaching act is to establish teaching objectives that serve as pivotal points from which all of the other teaching functions take on meaning. These objectives, however, become more meaningful for evaluation purposes when they are expressed in *behavioristic terms* (see Chapter 5).

All teachers engage in the identification and implementation of teaching objectives. This process may be conscious or unconscious, deliberate or unintentional. To evaluate teaching effectiveness with a reasonable degree of objectivity and accuracy, the evaluator can only concern himself with children's behaviors that develop intentionally as a result of a planned teaching act. During any mathematics lesson (as with lessons in other subject-matter areas), incidental, unintentional, peripheral objectives may be accomplished; but highly creative mathematics teaching cannot depend upon random and/or unintentional accomplishment of objectives. The quality of a mathematics lesson must be evaluated in terms of the predetermined objectives for the lesson. If the objectives have been poorly conceived, the lesson is seriously handicapped.

Ease of testing and evaluation are directly related to the specificity of objectives. The reader will discover that the more specifically objectives for a lesson are written, the easier it becomes to devise tests and evaluation procedures for those objectives.

Testing Children's Achievement in the Discovery Method of Teaching Mathematics

In order to plan future learning for students in an intelligent fashion, we, as mathematics teachers, need to test and measure student achievements. The conventional conception of testing in mathematics applies largely to testing the end product (the answer). Of course there will always be a need to do just that; it would be foolhardy not to be concerned with the accuracy of a solution to a mathematical problem. But standardized tests and the teacher-made variety tend not to test divergent thinking. In testing students' achievement in the discovery method of teaching, such tests are relevant only to step four. If we strive to promote a galaxy of answers or solutions from children, tests which look for a single "right" answer are often inappropriate.

Teacher-made and standardized tests that permit a wide range of "right answers" are needed for the teacher who desires to test the range of flexible creative thinking in children. At the present time, such tests are relatively scarce. Therein lies a challenge for the classroom teacher to develop tests to ascertain how many variations a child can make in an answer and still keep the answer within the realm of possibility.

The discovery process contains at least four steps. Thus far the galaxy of final solutions has applied only to step four. Tests that reflect children's behavior at steps one and three can yield revealing information as to children's creative thinking abilities.

It is in a student's sensitivity to and perception of the problem (step one) as well as in his experimental behavior (step three) that he reveals his openness to and facility with the creative process. The teacher who wants to assess the nature and scope of a child's creative thinking in the discovery *method* needs to collect evidence about the child's behavior relative to steps one and three of the discovery *process*.

Creativity involves a process and a product; so does the discovery method of teaching. This is one reason why this method is such a fine teaching vehicle for promoting creativity. As a teacher of mathematics, you need to be as concerned about the process a child uses to find an answer as about the answer itself. The end product is much easier to test and evaluate than the process. But a description of the child's thinking processes within the discovery method (steps one and three) can reveal the quantity of solutions the child considered before settling on an answer.

Teacher observation of student behavior in step one of the discovery method is one technique of collecting evidence (anecdotal in character). The verbal responses students give (number of and type) during the discussion of a mathematical problem constitute important data, and the technique of soliciting responses from children constitutes a type of informal testing.

It is possible to construct paper and pencil tests that will test a student's understanding of a mathematical problem. The test questions need to be phrased in such a way that the student is encouraged to individually brainstorm all of the ramifications of the problem that he can think of. After reading a mathematical word problem on the test, the students are *not* requested to compute an answer to the problem. (Now, this is a switch, isn't it?) Instead, there are some printed test questions about the mathematical problem itself. The test is not designed to see if the student can figure out a correct answer to the mathematical problem; its purpose is to ascertain how sensitively and flexibly the student perceives the mathematical problem. In other words, this test is aimed at obtaining some test data relative to step one of the discovery method. The test might consist of one mathematical word problem. The student is asked to answer questions about the word problem, such as:

1. Is there any information that is not given in the word problem that could affect the answer to it?
2. How many *different* algorisms can you construct which would depict the word problem?
3. Do you see any problems "within the problem" which should be considered?
4. If you could change the wording of the problem in any way you wanted, what changes would you make and why?

It is just as difficult to appraise students' achievement in step three of the discovery process as in step one. Step three involves ideation, flashes of insight, hunches, etc. Until we understand more fully the inner working of the mind, step three will remain somewhat of a mystery to the teacher and the student. If some type of elaborate machine that could trace the thought processes of a human being was available, we could gather some electronic data as to the complexities and subtleties of creative thinking. At present we will have to test step three through teacher observations of students and students' verbal descriptions of the mental processes they employ in solving mathematical problems. Trial and error certainly is employed by some students in step three, but it is the least sophisticated method of attacking a problem.

And so step three of the discovery method—the essence of

creative thinking—eludes and, at times, seems to defy analysis. An effective teacher can only set conditions for it to occur and attempt to observe and describe its nature.

Testing and Evaluating Mathematical Skills and Knowledges Creatively

Creativity can be used in determining the *manner* in which teachers test, measure, and evaluate the mathematics progress of their students. The job of the mathematics teacher is two-fold. Mathematics as a discipline contains a body of ideas and skills, many of which society expects children to master. Therefore, in addition to appraising the students' creative behavior in mathematics, the mathematics teacher needs to identify, test, measure and evaluate students' progress toward the acquisition of the knowledges and skills prescribed by the curriculum. Unfortunately, this job is the only one to which many mathematics teachers address themselves. They avoid the sticky task of attempting to appraise the quantity and quality of students' creative behavior in mathematics. Both tasks are important.

How Can a Teacher Be Creative in Testing, Measuring, and Evaluating Children's Progress in Mathematics?

It is impossible to tell someone "how to be creative." An act is classified as creative because of its relationship to the particular setting in which it occurs.

Rather than attempt the impossible, the authors elect to describe some variations and modifications of conventional testing, measuring, and evaluating procedures and devices. This may give the reader a general understanding of creative variations from conventional practice. The authors suggest that the reader engage in reference reading relative to the many varieties of tests, such as readiness tests, achievement tests, diagnostic tests, nonverbal tests, performance tests, etc. Likewise the reader will need to study the mechanics of test item construction; true-false, multiple-choice, completion, matching questions, etc.

Evaluation involves interpreting the measurement data so that the teacher and others concerned with the learner can form an accurate picture of the learner's performance in relation to his past performance, the performance of his peers, and national norms if they are available.

Examples of Creative Testing

The conventional method of attacking the testing task is to have children take a paper and pencil test of representative algorisms. Pencil and paper mathematics tests serve valuable purposes at times, but what other exciting materials and techniques might the teacher use to test his students? The following are some unusual techniques and devices that teachers have employed to test children relative to some aspect of mathematics:

Teacher A dictates a mathematics test on a tape recorder. Individually or in groups, children can listen to the test and work out the answers at their own speed.

Teacher B, a primary-level teacher, acts as store clerk for the play store set up in her classroom. One by one she asks the children to come to the store and shop for three items. She tells each child the cost of each item. The child, using paper and pencil, is requested to figure out how much he owes the store clerk. The papers upon which the children figure their bill serve as test papers.

Teacher C passes rhythm band instruments to each member of his class. He reads aloud a mathematical problem, allowing the class some time to think about the problem. The students are instructed to make a noise with their rhythm band instrument whenever they hear a correct answer to the problem. Then Teacher C reads aloud a list of possible answers. He makes mental notes of which children consistently make an incorrect response.

Teacher D acts as moderator for a mock television quiz game dealing with mathematical problems. The responses of individual children are recorded on a tape recorder throughout the game. Replaying the tape later enables Teacher D to determine which children seemed to be having difficulty with specific types of mathematical problems.

Teacher E uses a modification of the NUMBO game described in Chapter 2 as an informal test device.

Teacher F, using the opaque projector and some simple sketches, projects various groupings of objects on a screen. The children record on their papers number sentences that represent the groupings of objects projected on the screen.

Teacher G uses a puppet to administer a mathematics test. The puppet, dressed in a space pilot's suit, whispers in the teacher's ear each question for the test. Acting as central mission controller, the teacher repeats the puppet's directions to the students. The students compute on their papers various aspects of the "flight" as it is given to them by central control.

The number of methods of testing children in mathematics is limited only by the imagination of each teacher.

Creative Mathematical Devices *

To know is nothing at all; to imagine is everything.

ANATOLE FRANCE (1844–1924)

Creative Counters?

Most mathematics educators will agree that it is valuable for children in the elementary school to employ counters as a learning aid. Counters of some type provide a concrete material with which children can prove various mathematical solutions. Children in the elementary school often will use milk bottle caps, soda straws, pieces of colored paper, toothpicks, etc., for the purpose. By utilizing these simple counters, the teacher of mathematics can lead children to demonstrate "what happens" when we add, subtract, multiply, and divide.

* * *

One pitfall in the use of counters is that children are apt to become tired and bored using the same old things every day. Let's take a look at how Miss Glancy, a second-grade teacher, copes with this problem. As you might guess, on some days she simply has the children exchange counters so that if they were counting soda straws yesterday, today they use ice cream sticks. On some days Miss Glancy supplies special counters. She obtains these by cutting them out of colored paper or cardboard the day before. It takes very little time to do this, as many can be cut at one time if one folds the paper.

One autumn day Miss Glancy said to her class, "I'll supply the counters for today's mathematics lesson." The counters turned out to be made of colored paper in the shapes of acorns and pine cones. Another day, colored leaves were used. Funny faces were used near Halloween; witches and black cats turned up later. Several times during the school year Miss Glancy passed out paper napkins, and, after having the children wash their hands, distributed candy corn,

---

* Eleven written in ancient tallying method.

tiny red valentine heart candies, or gumdrops. After the children had utilized the candy counters in the math lesson, they were permitted to "eat their counters." All the children indicated that the mathematics lesson was "delicious."

Perhaps Miss Glancy's behavior in utilizing counters is of little consequence relative to the teaching of mathematics. It is true that the innovations just described are not earth-shaking in and of themselves. But Miss Glancy's desire to make innovations and modifications in such a routine matter as the use of counters represents the basic attitude of the highly creative teacher, who is, above all, unpredictable. The highly creative teacher constantly looks for aspects of the classroom program which can be improved or varied to add interest. The fact that Miss Glancy varied the type of counters does not instantly classify her as a highly creative teacher. But, as a single behavior, it points in the direction of creativity. Naturally, one would need many more samples of Miss Glancy's teaching behavior before classifying her as a highly creative teacher of mathematics.

Place Value Devices

Place value is one of the basic elements of our number system. In fact, place values is the *keystone* of our number system. Children must understand it if they are to discover the inner workings of our system, as well as other number systems. One way of promoting accurate concepts and understandings in children about the nature of place value is to employ concrete teaching materials liberally. Such aids can be devised so as to illustrate graphically the mechanics of place value both in our decimal system and in systems using other bases. Sometimes you, in the role of mathematics teacher, will want to create place value teaching devices on your own. At other times, students who have an adequate background in place value should be stimulated to create original devices. The most common type of place value device is the pocket chart similar to the one shown in Figure 11–1. It can be constructed by gluing a strip of cardboard to another piece of cardboard in the manner indicated in the drawing.

A more creative place value device is shown in Figure 11–2. What fun it is for children to make such devices and then utilize them in mathematics activities! The device shown in Figure 11–2 is a cardboard barracks building. The barracks has a 100's door, a 10's

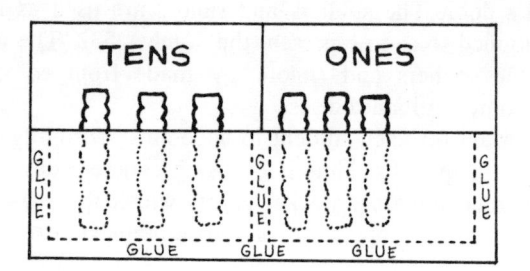

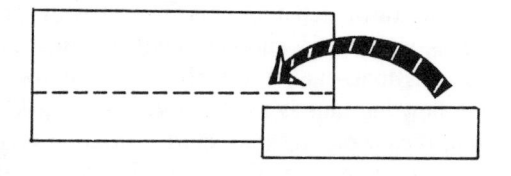

FIGURE 11–1. *Pocket chart used as place value device*

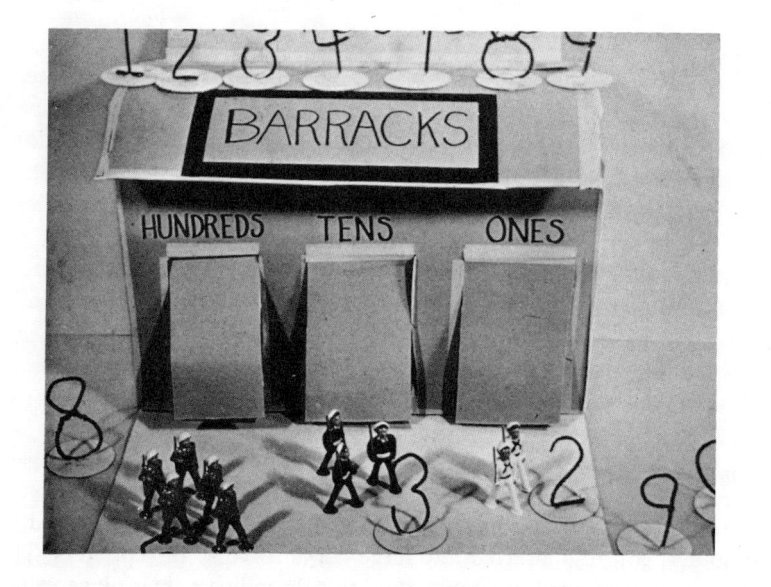

FIGURE 11–2. *Imaginative place value device*

door and a 1's door. The soldiers and sailors are used as markers. They are positioned so as to represent the number 532. The numerals shown with the soldiers and sailors are made from colored pipe cleaners glued onto cardboard discs.

It is important for each student to have an opportunity to prove mathematical principles for himself by using concrete devices. Children can construct miniature pocket charts which they can store in their desks for easy reference. Colored toothpicks can serve as markers.

Figure 11–3 is a slightly modified pocket chart that was developed by the teacher of a fourth grade. A strike in bowling, which means knocking down ten pins, fits in well with the "tens" idea of place value. And, just as another modification, cardboard bowling pins are used as markers for the chart. The number shown on the chart by the bowling pins is the number 25 (two 10's and five 1's). This bowling theme place value chart is a good example of "hitchhiking" a modification from the basic idea of a pocket place value device.

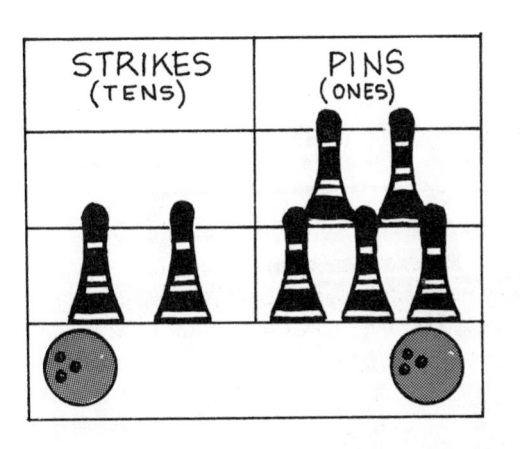

FIGURE 11–3. *Slight modification of conventional pocket chart*

Another Variation of the Theme

A place value device can be constructed with a piece of pegboard as a holder; golf tees inserted into large corks serve as the counters. The corks can be painted different colors to help indicate their place value.

As illustrated in Figure 11–4, simple electronics could be in-

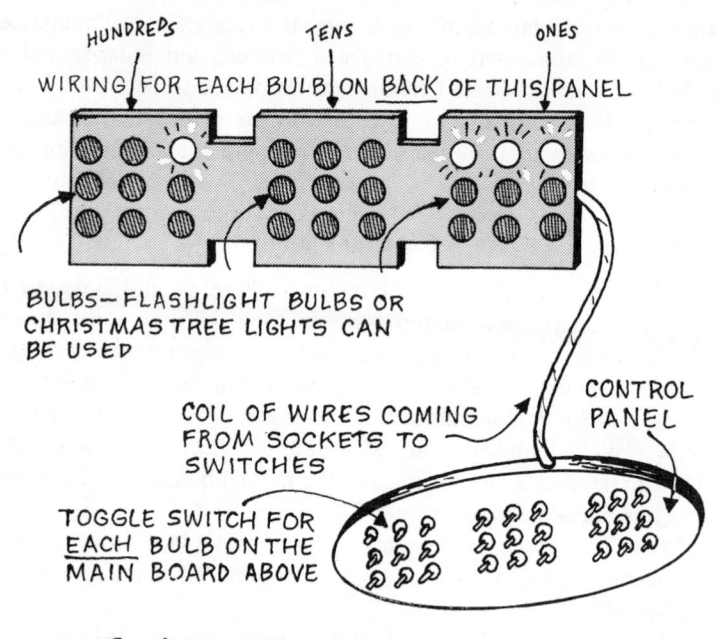

HUNDREDS TENS ONES

WIRING FOR EACH BULB ON BACK OF THIS PANEL

BULBS—FLASHLIGHT BULBS OR CHRISTMAS TREE LIGHTS CAN BE USED

COIL OF WIRES COMING FROM SOCKETS TO SWITCHES

CONTROL PANEL

TOGGLE SWITCH FOR EACH BULB ON THE MAIN BOARD ABOVE

THE LIGHTS THAT ARE ON DENOTE THE NUMBER 103

FIGURE 11–4. *Electric place value device*

corporated into a place value device. The electronic place value device shown in the drawing is made of thin plywood and pegboard. A 6-volt transformer will cut down regular 110-volt house current so that children can work safely with it. Dry cell batteries connected together could be used in place of the 6-volt transformer to supply enough direct current to run the circuits. Students who might tackle the task of creating an electronic place value device will also have to create some type of circuitry to suit the device. What other ways can you think of to incorporate electronics and the principle of place value? There is a great sense of achievement for the teacher and his students when they create original mathematics materials.

It would be ridiculous to suggest that the reader create his own mathematical teaching devices and then proceed to describe precisely how to create them. The mathematics teaching aids that are described on these pages are presented only to exemplify some home-made mathematics materials from which you, the reader, may "hitchhike" an idea or be stimulated to produce a teaching aid independent of any design presented here. Creation grows out of some type of need fulfillment. Because this is so, it will be during your actual classroom teaching of mathematics that ideas for original teaching aids will germinate.

Old "Friends" Employed in Different Ways

Place value devices that are interest-provoking do not have to be unique. Frequently new methods of dressing up time-worn devices are highly effective in adding a new touch to a mathematics lesson. The flannel board and the magnetic board are far from being new teaching aids for mathematics, but the highly creative teacher looks for new ways to employ such old friends as these. Remember Miss Ladd, who devised a modified use of the flannel board with her flower and its removable petals (Chapter 4).

Many household implements can serve as place value devices. Egg cartons and muffin tins are two examples. What other ones can you think of?

The hen house illustrated in Figure 11–6 and the corral in Figure 11–7 are two more ideas for basic place value devices.

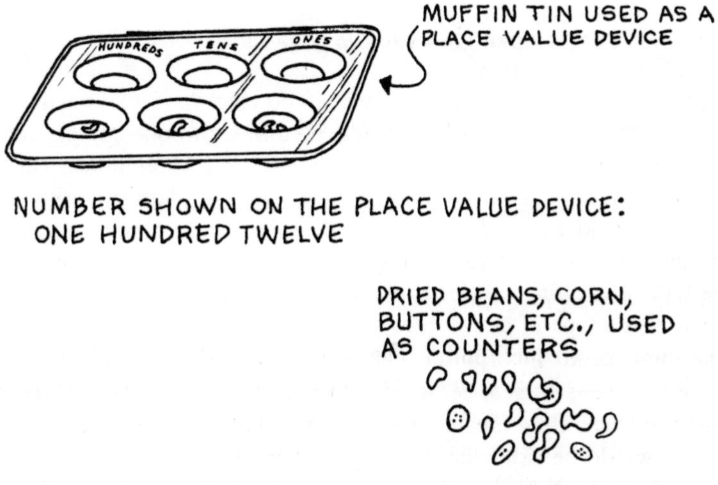

MUFFIN TIN USED AS A PLACE VALUE DEVICE

NUMBER SHOWN ON THE PLACE VALUE DEVICE:
ONE HUNDRED TWELVE

DRIED BEANS, CORN, BUTTONS, ETC., USED AS COUNTERS

FIGURE 11–5. *Muffin tin as place value device*

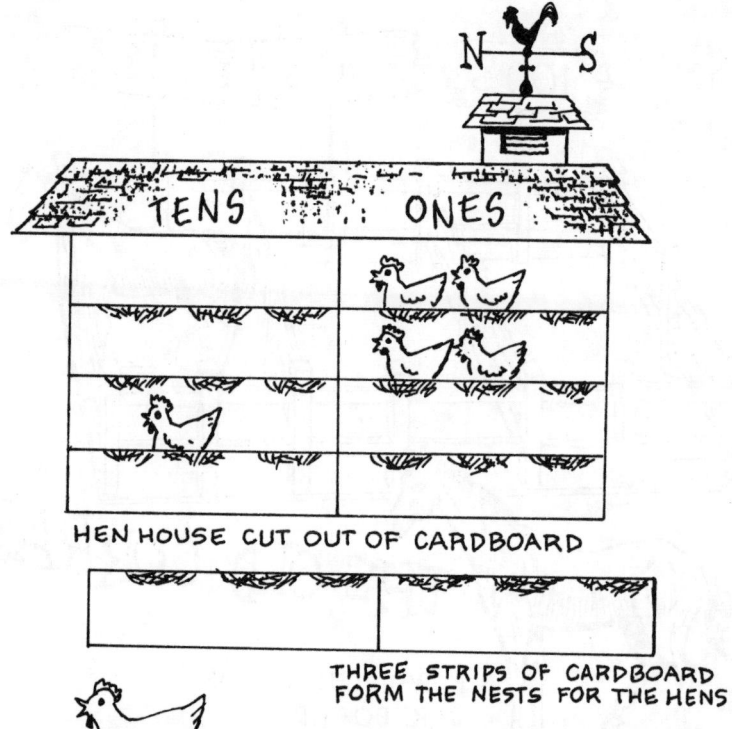

HEN HOUSE CUT OUT OF CARDBOARD

THREE STRIPS OF CARDBOARD
FORM THE NESTS FOR THE HENS

HENS CUT FROM CARDBOARD
SERVE AS COUNTERS

NUMBER INDICATED SHOWN IN HEN HOUSE —— 14

FIGURE 11–6. *Hen house place value device*

Binary Place Value Device (Electric)

Electricity is wonderfully congruent with the characteristics of the binary numeration system. The binary numeration system employs only two symbols, usually 1 and 0, which can be associated with an electric light or an electric current being on or off.

If your students are working on the mechanics of a binary numeration system, you may want to encourage them to create vari-

THE OLD CORRAL

HORSE CUT OUT OF
CARDBOARD

FIGURE 11–7. *Corral place value device*

ous types of place value devices which can indicate place value utilizing a binary system. Similar devices can be designed for numeration systems using other bases. A binary place value device constructed by two fifth-grade boys is shown in Figure 11–8.

The electrical workings of this binary box (n_2) are very simple. It was made with bulbs and sockets from Christmas tree lights, a roll of wire, and some switches.

Folded Paper Place Value Device

A sheet of paper, folded as if you were going to make a fan, can serve as a handy and economical place value device. Each student

FIGURE 11–8. *Binary electric place value device*

can assemble one so that he can have it at his desk for easy reference. Buttons, dried beans, or corn can be used as markers—as well as jelly beans! Young children should be encouraged to place the folded paper place value device on their desks in such a way that the 1's place is on the right-hand side, which corresponds with the place values as we read and write numbers. It is less confusing for many young children to work with the folded paper device when the 1's are on this side. As shown in Figure 11–9, it may be helpful to some children to write the place designations inside each pocket (e.g., 1's, 10's, 100's place).

Hundreds of variations can be made in this simple device to make it more attractive and utilitarian. Certainly it could be adapted to demonstrate the place value mechanics of number systems with bases other than 10.

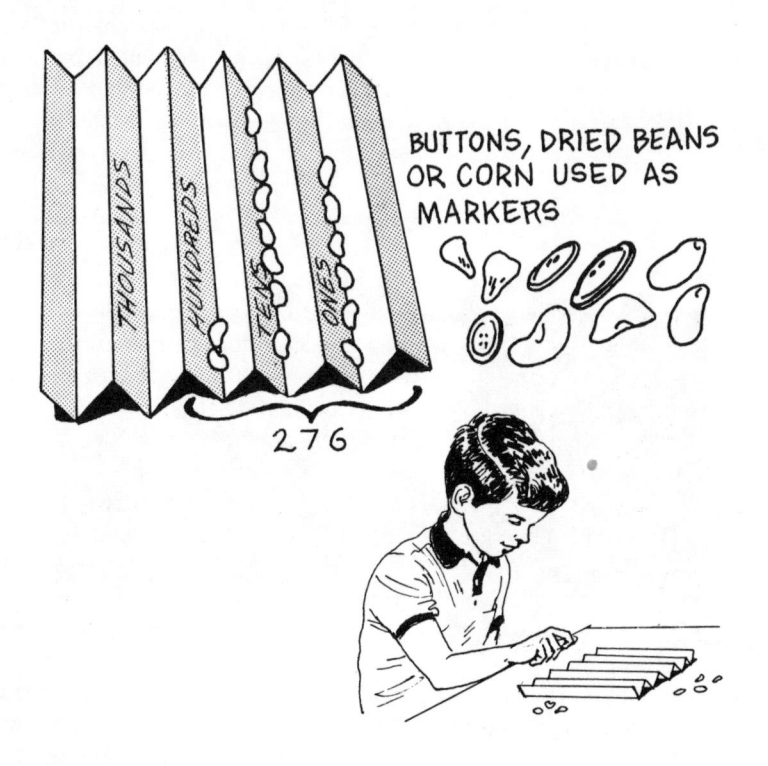

FIGURE 11–9. *Place value device of folded paper*

Abaci or Abacuses

The abacus is a type of place value device. Its original purpose was as a counter and simple computer. The exact origin of the abacus is lost in antiquity, but we do have evidence that the abacus was used over 2500 years ago by the ancient Egyptians, Babylonians, and Greeks. The basic idea of the abacus was carried to the Orient, where it was modified and widely circulated in China and Japan.

While the basic idea of the abacus was being carried from culture to culture it took on many different shapes and names. Its fundamental operation, however, has remained unchanged.

Although the abacus served ancient man as a highly utilitarian device, it is theorized that it hindered the development of zero. The abacus does not require any type of marker or symbol for zero. Many centuries passed before man developed a number system that was self-contained, one that did not need to be supplemented by some type of mechanical device. With the invention of the symbol for zero, man possessed a complete system for whole numbers. Many mathematicians and historians feel that the invention of the symbol for zero is one of the most significant accomplishments of man's intellect.

While the abacus may have been a deterrent to the invention of zero, it still provided a functional device for computing at a time when most number systems were cumbersome and inefficient. The abacus remains a helpful mathematical tool in many parts of the world today. In fact, some types of modern electronic computers work on the same general principle as the ancient abacus. The abacus can also be useful to the teacher and student of mathematics by serving as a device upon which the student can demonstrate the four basic processes of mathematics.

To develop a flexible concept of the abacus, children, as they progress through the elementary school, should be exposed to many types of abaci. They should also be encouraged to create their *own* types of abaci using whatever materials they can obtain.

The Japanese and Chinese developed the two rather sophisticated abaci pictured in Figure 11–10.

Both abaci have a crossbar against which a numeral is depicted; the beads above the crossbar indicate five units. So the numeral shown on the Chinese abacus is 66,012, and the numeral shown on the Japanese abacus is 200,605. The abacus still enjoys great popularity among the people of China and Japan; though no longer used in the Orient as the primary computer, it is still a mark of education to be proficient in using the abacus. There are private abacus schools, and many Oriental families send their children to private abacus lessons just as children in this country might take private music or ballet lessons. After a great deal of intensive practice, highly skilled Oriental abacus operators, when pitted against an electronic calculator, have demonstrated that they can calculate as rapidly as the calculator provided that the numerals involved are not very large ones.

You and your students may want to experiment with other modifications of the basic abacus idea. A student in the fifth grade designed the 2-cent abacus shown in Figure 11–11. Her explanation of the device included the fact that the estimated cost of the materials in the abacus was 2 cents. She also stressed the advantages of having such a little, portable abacus. The frame of the abacus is constructed from

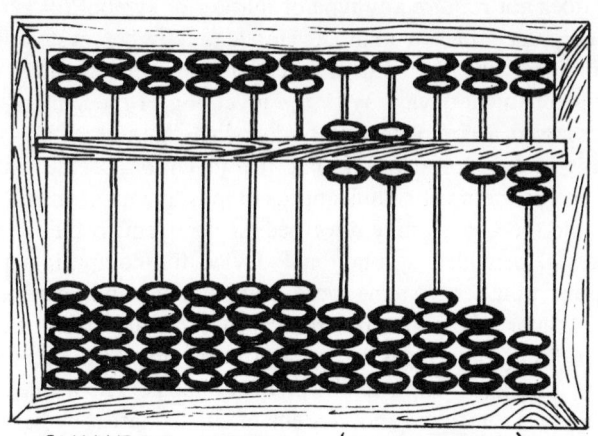

CHINESE ABACUS (SUAN PAN)

JAPANESE ABACUS

FIGURE 11–10. *Chinese and Japanese abaci*

cardboard; the "rods" are of string; the counters are pieces of colored macaroni; and the crossbar is a rubber band.

Designing an original abacus can be a creative experience for students.

2¢ ABACUS

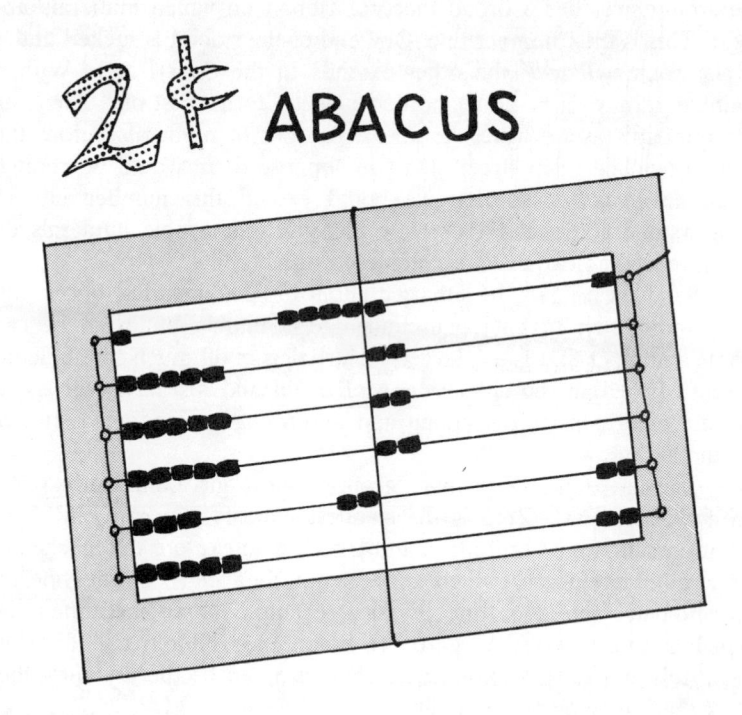

FIGURE 11–11. *Child's portable abacus*

Number Lines

As we have emphasized repeatedly, one element that is conducive to creativity is the quality of open-endedness. And nothing is more open-ended than a number line; children in elementary school can be fascinated and excited by a creative introduction to the number line and its characteristics.

* * *

Miss Pollard compares the number line in her classroom to Jack's beanstalk; a child could walk along it all his life and never reach the end.

"How far can this number line be extended before I run out of numbers?" Mr. McDonald asks his fourth-grade class. Across the classroom stretches a broad piece of ribbon on which numerals appear. This is their number line. One end of the ribbon is tucked under a classroom window; the other extends to the door frame. With a twinkle in his eye, he adds another question to his first one. "Spacing the numerals as we have, would we run out of numerals before the ribbon reached main street? Do you suppose there would be enough numerals available so that we could extend this number line to Yellowstone National Park? How many Hindu-Arabic numerals do we have available to us to use along our number line?"

Sandy, who is often lethargic about his mathematics, blurts out, "My father says that no one can name a number but what he can name a number that is one larger." This triggers off much spontaneous discussion within the class. Mr. McDonald and his class will spend several class periods discussing and describing the characteristics of a number line.

In Miss Pollard's primary group, a little girl confidently states to her classmates, "Zero is the smallest number you can get." This is an opening for Miss Pollard and her class to explore the mechanics of a number line on which zero is not the "end" of the line. A thermometer serves as one practical example of an instrument on which numbers less than zero are recorded. Children can discover from this and related experiences that zero can be the *middle* rather than the beginning of a number line.

Creative Number Lines

There are at least three major elements of a number line which can be varied:

1. The construction of the number line in terms of the materials that are used.
2. The type of notation (binary, ancient Egyptian, Roman, etc.) that is employed.
3. The way the line is graduated into linear units.

There are other less significant elements that are also subject to variation, but the authors will confine themselves to illustrating two of the primary variables.

Varying the Material Construction of the Number Line

If your class is familiar with the mechanics of brainstorming, it may be useful to brainstorm variations of the number line. Figure 11–12 contains some suggestions for modifying the basic construction of number lines. These suggestions can serve as "sparks" for the reader to create modifications of his own.

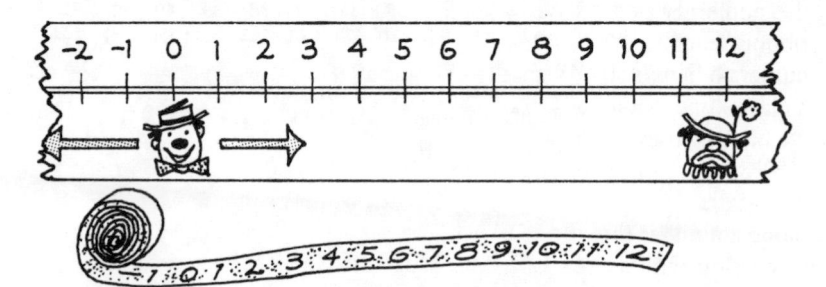

NUMBER LINE CAN BE MADE FROM ROLL OF WALL PAPER BORDER OR A ROLL OF WIDE MASKING TAPE OR A ROLL OF WIDE RIBBON OR A ROLL OF . . . .

PAPER CLIPS STRUNG ON A LENGTH OF WIRE. PAPER CLIPS HOLD NUMBER CARDS.

PIECE OF ROPE OR TINSEL — PINCHER-TYPE CLOTHES PINS HOLD ON NUMBER CARDS.

FIGURE 11–12. *Examples of number line modifications*

The number line in Figure 11–13 illustrates the second variable element of a number line—the type of notation that is employed. This number line contains the Hindu-Arabic numbers 28 through 42. It also indicates 28 through 42 in quinary numeration, mod 5, and ancient Egyptian notation.

What kind of interest-provoking number line can you create? Do number lines have to be horizontal? How many dimensions can a number line have? Are they always linear dimensions?

MODULUS 5

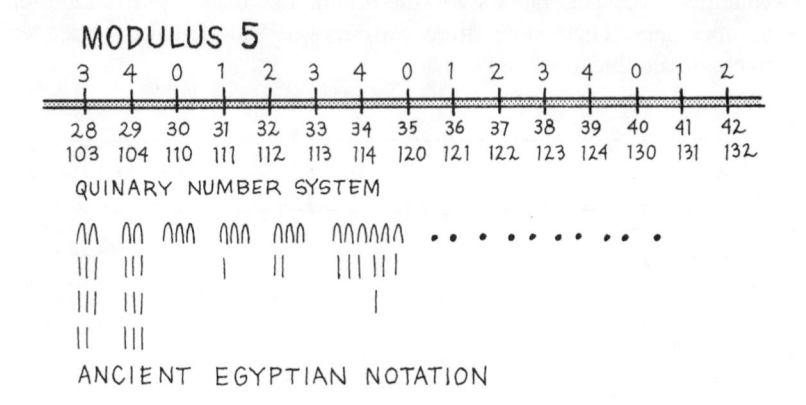

QUINARY NUMBER SYSTEM

ANCIENT EGYPTIAN NOTATION

FIGURE 11–13. *Using different types of notation in a number line*

Simple electrical circuits can be incorporated into an electronic number line. As we have shown in regard to place value devices, children in the intermediate levels of the elementary school can plan and construct a number line that correlates simple electricity principles with mathematics. Here again, a 6-volt transformer can make the regular household current safe for the children, or dry cell batteries can be employed. Each number on the number line is represented by a small electric bulb. A piece of wooden molding or firing strip can serve as the base for the number line. The wiring can be stapled to the back of the wooden number line. A lot of creativity and short circuits can go into working out the wiring for the electronic number line.

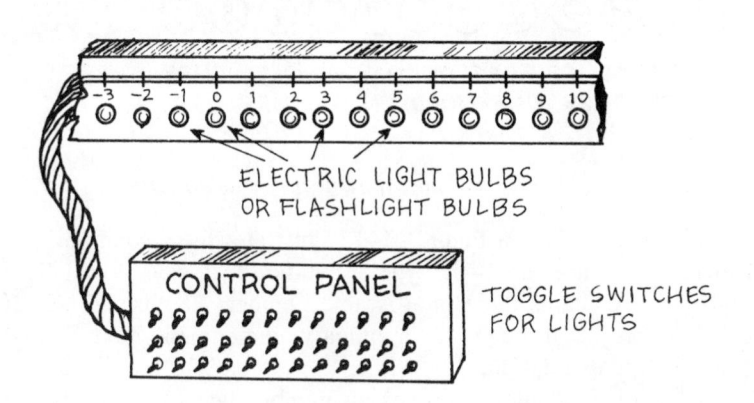

FIGURE 11–14. *Electronic number line*

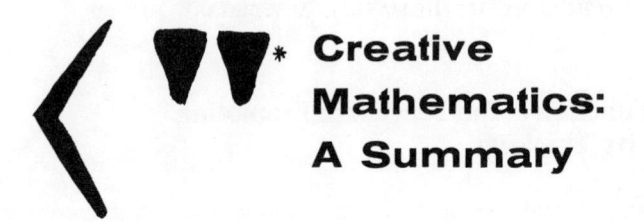

Creative Mathematics: A Summary

No great thing is created suddenly, any more than a bunch of grapes or a fig. If you tell me that you desire a fig, I answer you that there must be time. Let it first blossom, then bear fruit, then ripen.

EPICTETUS, *Discourses,* Chapter 15

Creativity and the Teacher

Creativity is special human magic. It is the mental activity that dramatically sets man apart from any other form of animal life. Human creativity has produced literally every technological and artistic innovation that is a part of man's contrived environment. Both creativity in general and creativity in mathematics involve a mental process in which any individual can engage to *some* extent. Because of this fact, the difference between a person who is labelled "very creative" by his peers and one labelled "not very creative" becomes a matter of degree. It is a relative measure. And of course this relative measure applies to creativity in mathematics, as well.

Creativity involves a projection of one's unique self. It involves a flexible and open-minded approach to problems. Ideally, a highly creative person can be highly creative in any area if certain variables are favorable.

One of the fascinating aspects of studying about creative thinking and creative behavior relative to mathematics is that it is shrouded in a great deal of mystery. A truly scientific analysis and description of the creative process has yet to be attained; a host of questions relative to creativity are unanswered; many avenues for investigation of the creative process are open-ended. Investigating the creative process constitutes a frontier of knowledge. As an elementary classroom teacher, you will be in the enviable position of being able to observe the creative behavior of children first-hand.

* Babylonian symbol for twelve.

The Function of the Teacher in Promoting Creative Thinking

The fundamental task of the teacher who would promote creativity in students is to develop in them the attitude (habit) of exploring the variability elements of the problem, media, task, or whatever is being considered. The variability elements refer to the modifications and changes that can be applied. The teacher who acts as a stimulator of creativity says to herself as well as to her class: How can this be changed? What are some other ways of looking at this problem?

The Basic Responsibility of Teaching Mathematics Creatively

The teacher himself need not be a highly creative person in order to stimulate and promote creative thinking in his pupils. But, first and foremost, he must strive to stimulate genuine pupil interest in mathematics. This factor is one of the vital keys to mathematical creation in children. High interest is primary to the creative act. Great knowledge about the task to be accomplished is insignificant at the outset of creative effort, but keen interest is indispensable. The teacher of mathematics needs to exude enthusiasm for his subject in order for children to catch the spark. Then he will be serving as a catalyst to stimulate creative thinking in his students.

What Constitutes Creativity in Mathematics?

Of all the questions that pertain to creativity in mathematics, this one evokes the most agreement among mathematics educators. The exact nature of the creative *process* eludes scientific definition at this writing, but almost no one disputes what a creative *product* in mathematics *is*.

Creativity in mathematics is the birth or discovery of new number patterns; the development of new relationships between mathematical ideas; the modification and/or variance of existing patterns, symbols, and relationships; the contrivance of new symbolism and organization of symbols; the discovery of new applications of mathematical ideas. As mathematics is in reality a system of related ideas, so creativity in mathematics can be simply defined as the production of new relationships.

Is There a Special Talent for Mathematics?

It has been believed for many years that there is a special talent for mathematics and that it can be inherited, like color of hair or color of eyes. The implication, of course, is that special mathematical talent is carried via genetic accident. To date, there is no conclusive research evidence to indicate that a special talent for mathematics exists. Rather than a single talent especially related to mathematics, there appear to be special combinations of human personality variables related to unusual competence in mathematics. Various combinations of these human variables determine the extent to which an individual is capable of engaging in creative mathematics. Thus creative ability relative to mathematics becomes a matter of degree rather than an absolute.

There has been some interesting research regarding the personality variables related to mathematical achievement. Findings indicate that innate intelligence seems to contribute the most to mathematical achievement. The three general human variables which interact to determine an individual's level of creativity in mathematics are:

1. Intelligence (innate intelligence, not necessarily that which is measured by existing intelligence tests).
2. Personality
3. Interest (motivation)

You will note that previous knowledge about mathematics is not considered to be an important variable. This conclusion was reached as a result of research in related areas as to the importance of facts in the creative process.

Is the Accumulation of Mathematical Facts Conducive to Creative Thinking in Mathematics?

. . . it is helpful to speculate about the relationship between creative performance and the sheer accumulation of knowledge. It is easy to cite examples of people in the academic world who are well versed in their fields but who have demonstrated little creativity. One also can name productive and creative persons who are criticized by scholars for not being well read or for not giving due veneration to past knowledge and to the accepted orientations in their field. In other words, sheer mastery of knowledge does not seem to be a sufficient condition for creative performance.[1]

Many psychologists, educators, and persons interested in the area of creativity hold to the premise that creativity and mathematics have a unique relationship. This relationship hinges on the fact that creation in mathematics, as compared to creation in the arts and sciences, appears to be the least dependent upon the environment and the earthly experiences of the creator.

Henri Poincaré states it this way:

> The genesis of mathematical creation is a problem which should intensely interest the psychologist. It is that activity in which the human mind seems to take least from the outside world, in which it acts or seems to act only of itself and on itself. . . .[2]

In General, Have Teachers Progressed Toward Highly Creative and Functional Teaching of Mathematics?

Obviously, this question contains many ambiguities. It raises many other questions, such as: What constitutes progress? The authors leave the resolution of this question with the reader.

Perhaps this excerpt from *The District School As It Was,* by Reverend Warren Burton, will be of assistance. The Reverend Burton described his rural school experiences in Wilton, New Hampshire, from 1804 until he left the school in the winter term of 1817–1818. Here are some of his thoughts relative to the teaching and learning of arithmetic:

> At the age of twelve, I commenced the study of Arithmetic, that chiefest of sciences in Yankee estimation. No man is willing that his son should be without skill in figures. And if he does not teach him his ABC at home, he will the art of counting, at least. Many a father deems it no hardship to instruct his child to enumerate even up to a hundred, when it would seem beyond his capacity, or certainly beyond the leisure of his rainy days and winter evenings, to sit down with the formality of a book, and teach him to read.
> The entering on arithmetic was quite an era in my school-boy life. This was placing me decidedly among the great boys, and within hailing distance of manhood. My feelings were consequently considerably elevated. A new Adams's Arithmetic of the latest edition was bought for my use. It was covered by the maternal hand with stout sheepskin, in the

[1] Calvin W. Taylor, *Creativity: Progress and Potential* (New York: McGraw-Hill Book Company, 1964).

[2] Henri Poincaré, "Mathematical Creation," in *The Creative Process,* Brewster Ghiselin, ed. (Berkeley, Calif.: University of California Press, 1952).

economical expectation, that, after I had done with it, it might help still younger heads to the golden science. A quire of foolscap was made to take the form of a manuscript of the full length of the sheet, with a pasteboard cover, as more suitable to the dignity of such superior dimensions than flimsy brown paper. . . .

My first exercise was transcribing from my Arithmetic to my manuscript. At the top of the first page I penned ARITHMETIC, in capitals an inch high, and so broad that this one word reached entirely across the page. At a due distance below, I wrote the word ADDITION in large, coarse hand, beginning with a lofty A, which seemed like the drawing of a mountain peak, towering above the level wilderness below. Then came *Rule,* in a little smaller hand, so that there was a regular gradation from the enormous capitals at the top, down to the fine running—no, hobbling hand in which I wrote off the rule.

Now slate and pencil and brain came into use. I met with no difficulty at first; Simple Addition was as easy as counting my fingers. But there was one thing I could not understand—that carrying of tens. It was absolutely necessary, I perceived, in order to get the right answer; yet it was a mystery which that arithmetical oracle, our schoolmaster, did not see fit to explain. It is possible that it was a mystery to him. Then came Subtraction. The borrowing of ten was another unaccountable operation. The reason seemed to me then at the very bottom of the well of science; and there it remained for that winter, for no friendly bucket brought it up to my reach. . . .

The end of the Arithmetic seemed almost as far off in the future as that end of boyhood and under-age restraint, twenty-one.

The next winter I began at Addition again, to advance just through Interest. My third season I went over the same ground again, and, besides that, ciphered to the very last sum in the Rule of Three. This was deemed quite an achievement for a lad only fourteen years old, according to the ideas prevailing at that period. Indeed, whoever ciphered through the above-mentioned rule was supposed to have arithmetic enough for the common purposes of life. If one proceeded a few rules beyond this, he was considered quite smart. . . .

The female portion of the school, we may suppose, generally expected to obtain husbands to perform whatever arithmetical operations they might need, beyond the counting of fingers: so the science found no special favor with them. If pursued at all, it was neglected till the last year or two of their schooling. Most were provident enough to cipher as far as through the four simple rules; for although they had no idea of becoming old maids, they might possibly, however, be left widows. Had arithmetic been pursued at the summer school, those who intended to be summer teachers would probably have thought more of the science, and have proceeded further, even perhaps to the Rule of Three. But a schoolmistress would as soon have expected to teach the Arabic language as the numerical science. . . .[3]

[3] Warren Burton, *The District School As It Was,* ed. by Clifton Johnson (New York: Thomas Y. Crowell Company, 1928).

Bibliography

ADAMS, GEORGIA S. and T. L. TORGESON. *Measurement and Evaluation in Education, Psychology, and Guidance.* New York: Holt, Rinehart and Winston, Inc., 1964.

ANDERSON, HAROLD H. (ed.). *Creativity and Its Cultivation.* New York: Harper & Row, Inc., 1959.

BANKS, J. HOUSTON. *Learning and Teaching Arithmetic.* Boston: Allyn and Bacon, Inc., 1964.

BEAUCHAMP, GEORGE. *The Curriculum of the Elementary School.* Boston: Allyn and Bacon, Inc., 1964.

BURTON, WILLIAM H. *The Guidance of Learning Activities.* New York: Appleton-Century-Crofts, Inc., 1952.

CORLE, CLYDE G. *Teaching Mathematics in the Elementary School.* New York: The Ronald Press Company, 1964, pp. 166–202.

CRESCIMBENI, JOSEPH. *Arithmetic Enrichment Activities for Elementary School Children.* West Nyack: Parker Publishing Company, Inc., 1965.

DUTTON, WILBUR H. *Evaluating Pupils' Understanding of Arithmetic.* Englewood Cliffs: Prentice-Hall, Inc., 1964.

EBEL, ROBERT L. *Measuring Educational Achievement.* Englewood Cliffs: Prentice-Hall, Inc., 1965.

Evaluation in Mathematics. Washington, D.C.: Twenty-sixth Yearbook of the National Council of Teachers of Mathematics, 1961.

FEHR, HOWARD F. and THOMAS J. HILL. *Contemporary Mathematics for Elementary Teachers.* Boston: D. C. Heath and Co., 1966.

GETZELS, JACOB and PHILLIP JACKSON. *Creativity and Intelligence: Explorations with Gifted Students.* New York: John Wiley & Sons, Inc., 1962.

GHISELIN, BREWSTER (ed.). *The Creative Process.* New York: Mentor Books, 1955; Berkeley, Calif.: University of California Press, 1952.

GLENNON, VINCENT (ed.). *What Does Research Say About Arithmetic?* Washington, D.C.: Association for Supervision and Curriculum Development, National Education Association, 1952.

GREEN, JOHN A. *Teacher-Made Tests.* New York: Harper & Row, Inc., 1963.

GROSSNICKLE, FOSTER E. and LEO J. BRUECKNER. *Discovering Meanings in Elementary School Mathematics.* New York: Holt, Rinehart and Winston, Inc., 1963.

GRUBER, HOWARD E., GLENN TERRELL, and MICHAEL WERTHEIMER (eds.). *Contemporary Approaches to Creative Thinking.* New York: Atherton Press, 1962.

GUILFORD, J. P. "The Structure of the Intellect," *Psychological Bulletin,* 1956.

HUNNICUTT, C. W. and WILLIAM J. IVERSON. *Research in the Three R's.* New York: Harper & Row, Inc., 1958.

215

KNELLER, GEORGE F. *The Art and Science of Creativity.* New York: Holt, Rinehart and Winston, 1965.

KOESTLER, ARTHUR. *The Act of Creation.* New York: The Macmillan Company, 1964.

KRAMER, KLAAS. *Mathematics for the Elementary School Teacher.* Boston: Allyn and Bacon, Inc., 1965.

KUBIE, L. S. *Neurotic Distortion of the Creative Process.* Lawrence: University of Kansas Press, 1958.

LOWENFELD, VIKTOR. *Creative and Mental Growth* (3rd ed.). New York: The Macmillan Co., 1957.

MARKS, JOHN L., RICHARD PURDY and LUCIEN B. KINNEY. *Teaching Elementary School Mathematics for Understanding* (2nd ed.). New York: McGraw-Hill Book Co., 1965.

MARKSBERRY, MARY LEE. *Foundations of Creativity.* New York: Harper & Row, 1963.

MARTIN, R. LEE and ALVIN M. WESTCOTT. *Gateway to Teaching.* Dubuque, Iowa: William C. Brown Co., 1963, Chapter 5.

MCFARLAND, DORA and EUNICE M. LEWIS. *Introduction to Modern Mathematics.* Boston: D. C. Heath and Co., 1966.

MIEL, ALICE (ed.). *Creativity in Teaching: Invitations and Instances.* Belmont, Calif.: Wadsworth Publishing Co., 1961.

PARNES, S. J. and A. MEADOW. "Effects of Brainstorming Instructions in Creative Problem-solving by Trained and Untrained Subjects," *Journal of Educational Psychology,* 1959, pp. 171–176.

QUINN, DANIEL (ed.). *A Guide to Modern Mathematics.* Chicago: Science Research Associates, 1964.

RUGG, HAROLD. *Imagination: An Inquiry Into the Sources and Conditions That Stimulate Creativity.* New York: Harper & Row, 1963.

RUSSELL, DAVID H. *Children's Thinking.* Boston: Ginn and Company, 1956.

SCHOOL MATHEMATICS STUDY GROUP. *Mathematics for the Elementary School.* Stanford University Press, 1963.

SHIPP, DONALD E. and SAM ADAMS. *Developing Arithmetic Concepts and Skills.* Englewood Cliffs, N.J.: Prentice-Hall, Inc., 1965, pp. 282–288.

SHUMSKY, ABRAHAM. *Creative Teaching in the Elementary School.* New York: Appleton-Century-Crofts, Inc., 1965.

SWAIN, ROBERT L. *Understanding Arithmetic.* New York: Holt, Rinehart and Winston, 1965.

SWENSEN, ESTHER J. *Teaching Arithmetic to Children.* New York: The Macmillan Company, 1964.

TAYLOR, CALVIN (ed.). *Creativity: Progress and Potential.* New York: McGraw-Hill Book Company, 1964.

TORRANCE, E. PAUL. *Gifted Children in the Classroom.* New York: The Macmillan Company, 1965.

TORRANCE, E. PAUL. *Guiding Creative Talent.* Englewood Cliffs: Prentice-Hall, Inc., 1962.

TORRANCE, E. PAUL. *Rewarding Creative Behavior.* Englewood Cliffs: Prentice-Hall, Inc., 1965.

TRAVERS, ROBERT M. *How to Make Achievement Tests.* New York: The Odyssey Press, 1950.

WESTCOTT, ALVIN and JOHN SCHLUEP. *Fun With Timothy Triangle.* Mankato, Minnesota: Oddo Publishing Company, 1966.

Index

Abaci, 202–205
Abstract materials, 18, 22
Action in mathematics, 34–35
  take away, 53
Addition, 36
  basic combinations, 37
  basic concepts of, 37, 47–48
  binary numeration, 43–44
  bridging, 41
  checks for, 48–49
  devices and gadgets, 50–52
  higher decade, 41
  modular, 44
  organization of, 38
  readiness related to, 36–37
  upward or downward, 41
  variations of, 43
  with slide rule, 52
Addo game, 28–30
Ancient notation:
  addition of, 45
  fractions, 101–102
  multiplication of, 81
Anso game, 29–30
Ashton-Warner, Sylvia, 24
Associative principle, 47
Autonomy:
  related to creative behavior, 14

Barone, Vincent, 78
Basic combinations:
  of addition, 38–40
  of multiplication, 74–75
  of subtraction, 53–55, 59–61
Binary numeration:
  addition with, 43–44
  data processing, 164–165

Binary numeration (*Cont.*)
  multiplication with, 81
  place value device, 199–201
Brainstorming:
  in multiplication, 76
  in problem-solving, 117–120
Burton, Warren, 212–213

Charts:
  sets, 171–174
Checking accuracy:
  in addition, 48–50
  in subtraction, 70–72
Child:
  nature of, 11
Clock arithmetic; *see* Modular
  arithmetic
Color:
  algorisms in, 158
Commutative law:
  definition of, 75
  illustration of, 75
Concrete materials, 18
Coordinate system; *see* Graphing
Counters:
  creative mathematical, 193–194
Creative behavior:
  affected by need, 13
  and autonomy, 14–15
  observable, 13
  transfer of, 16
Creative individual:
  child, 11
  definition of, 3–4
  description of, 12
Creative teacher of mathematics,
  19–20